C000141993

HSC
Health & Safety
Commission

Health and Safety Commission
ANNUAL REPORT
1992/93

HSE BOOKS

ISBN 0 7176 0652 X

THE AIMS OF THE HEALTH AND SAFETY COMMISSION AND EXECUTIVE

The aims of the Health and Safety Commission and Executive, whose existence and functions derive from the Health and Safety at Work etc Act 1974, are to protect the health, safety and welfare of employees, and to safeguard others, principally the public, who may be exposed to risks from industrial activity.

The responsibility to take care is placed upon those directly engaged: mainly employers, but also the self-employed, suppliers etc. The Commission and Executive are there to inform, stimulate and guide those with duties of care, and others concerned with health and safety, in actions leading to higher standards; and in particular to:

(a)   define standards particularly by:
      (i)   proposing reform of existing legislation, through regulations and approved codes under the 1974 Act;
      (ii) issuing guidance; and
      (iii) co-operating with other standard-setting bodies;

(b)   participate, through negotiation, in relevant standard-setting in the European Community and in other international bodies, taking account of the principles of the 1974 Act;

(c)   promote compliance with the 1974 Act, and other legislation as relevant, in particular by:
      (i)   inspection, advice and enforcement in undertakings where HSE is the enforcing authority; and
      (ii) proposing arrangements for the allocation of enforcement responsibility as between HSE and other enforcement bodies; and keeping their effectiveness under review;

(d)   carry out, publish and promote research; and investigate accidents and industrial health problems, disseminating findings as appropriate;

(e)   provide specific services related to the Commission's main functions, eg an Employment Medical Advisory Service;

(f)   contribute to the processes of democratic decision-making, accountability and consistency of approach on health, safety and welfare issues, in particular by:
      (i)   providing advice and information as required to Ministers;
      (ii) co-operating with regulatory bodies in related fields;
      (iii) representing UK interests in EC and other inter-Governmental fora; and
      (iv) encouraging well-informed public discussion of the nature, scale and tolerability of risk.

The Commission and Executive's business is to see that risks from economic activity are controlled effectively, in ways that allow for technological progress and pay due regard to cost as well as benefits. They act in close consultation with all whom their work affects; and in all that they do, seek to promote better management of health and safety, through a systematic approach to identifying hazards and assessing and controlling risks.

CONTENTS

CHAIRMAN AND MEMBERS OF THE HEALTH AND SAFETY COMMISSION 1992/93

Chairman   The Chairman of the Health and Safety Commission is appointed by the Secretary of State for Employment.

Sir John Cullen F.Eng PhD was Chairman from October 1983 until his retirement in September 1993. He was in industry for 27 years, becoming European Director for Regulatory Affairs, Engineering and Health and Safety for ROHM and HAAS Limited.

Members   Members of the Health and Safety Commission are appointed by the Secretary of State for Employment after consultation with organisations representing employers, employees, local authorities and others as he/she thinks appropriate.

Councillor Eddie Carrick is Chairman of the Leisure and Recreation Committee, Vice Chairman of Staffing Committee of Stirling District Council and Vice Convenor of the Convention of Scottish Local Authorities' Environmental Services Committee. He has also been involved in safety standards and training in the construction industry.

Paul Gallagher has been President since 1987 of the Electrical, Electronic Telecommunications and Plumbing Union and is now General Secretary. He has wide negotiating experience in industry including engineering, contracting, local authorities and chemicals etc.

Peter Jacques CBE is Special Adviser to the TUC for matters including health, safety and environmental protection at work and is also a member of the Royal Commission on Environmental Pollution. He has been a member of the Health and Safety Commission since October 1974.

John C Marvin is Deputy Chairman of Whitecroft plc. Previously with Hickson International and ICI, his special interests are in relation to the Chemical Industries Association. *(To 31 March 1993)*

Nigel J Pitcher is a chartered engineer with wide experience in the contracting industry from petrochemical plants to motorways. He is a director of several Laing Group companies including Laing Engineering Limited and John Laing Construction.

Councillor Dr Colin Shannon CBE has been a member of the Suffolk Coastal District Council since 1974. He is a member of the Council of the Association of District Councils and is at present Chairman of its Environmental Health Committee. He has also been Vice-President of the Institute of Environmental Health Officers since 1983 and a member of the Health and Safety Commission since 1981. *(To 31 March 1993)*

Rex H M Symons was Deputy Chairman of Merck Holdings Limited from 1989 to 1991 and Managing Director of British Drug Houses Limited from 1980 - 89. He acts as the CBI's workplace health and safety consultant and is the Chairman of the Dorset Training and Enterprise Council.

Alan Tuffin is General Secretary of the Union of Communication Workers and a member of the TUC General Council. He is Chairman of the TUC's Social Health and Environment Committee. He has been a member of the Health and Safety Commission since October 1986.

Dame Rachel Waterhouse is the former Chairman of the Consumers Association. Currently council member, Association for Consumer Research; Chairman, Research Institute for Consumer Affairs; and President, Institute of Consumer Ergonomics. She has wide experience in consumer and social affairs, with a special interest in health and safety matters.

T Gates Secretary to the Health and Safety Commission.

NEW CHAIRMAN AND MEMBERS OF THE HEALTH AND SAFETY COMMISSION 1992/93

Appointed after the reporting year ended

Chairman

Frank J Davies CBE, O St J became Chairman of the Health and Safety Commission on 1 October 1993. He has over 40 years' experience of working in industry including construction, aluminium and glass manufacturing. He was Chief Executive of Rockware Group plc between 1983 and 1993 and is past-President of the European Glass Federation (FEVE). He is Chairman of the Nuffield Orthopaedic Centre NHS Trust.

Members

Christopher Chope OBE is a consultant for Ernst and Young, formerly a Minister at the Departments of Environment and Transport. In local government he has served as leader of Wandsworth Borough Council and on the London Boroughs Association, Association of Metropolitan Authorities and the former Inner London Education Authority. *(From 1 April 1993)*

Dr Geraldine Schofield is a senior microbiologist at Unilever Research. She is Project Leader on Expert Computer Systems in Microbiology, and has special responsibility for regulatory affairs in biotechnology. She belongs to the national Microbiological Consultative Committee on Safety as well as the Chemical Industries Association Biotechnology task force. *(From 25 June 1993)*

MEMBERS OF THE HEALTH AND SAFETY EXECUTIVE 1992/93

Director General **J D Rimington CB**
Appointed by the Commission with the approval of the Secretary of State for Employment

Deputy Director General **Miss J H Bacon**

Deputy Director General **D C T Eves**

The Deputy Directors General are appointed by the Commission with the approval of the Secretary of State and after consultation with the Director General

CHAIRMAN'S FOREWORD

This report covers my last full year as Chairman of the Health and Safety Commission. My services in that capacity have extended over a full decade, since I was appointed in October 1983; and in giving my final account, a quick background look over the longer perspective may be permissible.

The decade

Over the decade the trends of greatest importance have been:

- our steady acquisition of new responsibilities, including those for supervision of the Advisory Committee on Genetic Modification (1983), major new responsibilities for the control of major hazards under the Seveso Directive (1984), safety regulation of gas transmission (1985), much enlarged responsibilities under the Food and Environmental Protection Act for control of pesticides (1986), responsibilities as customer for nuclear safety research on established systems (1990) railway passenger safety (1990), and offshore safety (1991);

- a gradual shift of resources and interest towards occupational health and hygiene and a better appreciation of the consequences of occupational ill health in terms of time off work and premature retirement. The COSHH Regulations have provided the basic underpinning for more effective protection of the health of employees;

- a shift in the balance of our activities towards major hazards and the protection of the public from industrial harms, while fully maintaining our concern with the protection of employees.

- a much increased international commitment, expressed partly in a shift of focus to the European Community which now markedly determines our priorities and to an extent our policies;

- a marked increase in public concern for and in the subject matter of our work, and particularly its environmental aspects.

Offshore and railway safety

During the year under review, important developments took place under all these heads. Most importantly we achieved our first major objective in the legislative reform programme for offshore safety engendered by the Cullen Report on the Piper Alpha disaster, with the making of Safety Case Regulations in November 1992. We have pressed on with the huge task of overhauling and replacing the whole of the existing legislative structure, meeting all our objectives, and receiving, I am very glad to say, the full support and commitment of both sides of the offshore industry. We recognise the important steps the industry is itself taking to improve the safety culture offshore, and the immense contribution it is called upon to make to the endeavour on which we are jointly embarked, of making offshore installations a safer place.

The Commission also advised the Secretary of State for Transport at his request on the regulatory arrangements necessary for a privatised railway system, and our report and recommendations were accepted in full. This was a major task. The vast majority of those who commented on our proposals agreed with us that the arrangements we have in mind will fully maintain the protection both of the travelling public and members of railway staff.

The coal industry

We have in recent years put forward a large number of proposals for the modernisation of mines safety legislation, which have been designed to maintain and improve safety standards under changing conditions. During the year, the Commission's advice was also sought on a safety regime for a privatised coal industry.

European activity

The year was remarkable for the continuing high level of activity in terms of European and wider international work, including the introduction of six major regulations - the 'six-pack'- implementing previously agreed European directives. Although long foreseen, their coming into force simultaneously on 1 January 1993 understandably provoked a considerable reaction in terms of the imposed load on industry. There were suggestions - happily since refuted by a Department of Trade and Industry scrutiny on recent European legislation - that the Commission had exaggerated in its implementing measures the provisions of the directives. I should make it quite clear that our aim during the negotiations was always to secure provisions that were no more than proportionate to the risks involved and so far as possible in line with existing UK provisions. A good deal of success was in fact achieved in these respects, often under difficult conditions.

Generally, while we have strongly welcomed opportunities to achieve greater approximation of health and safety law and higher standards across Europe, the work done on our behalf to influence activity post - 1992 in the European communities has been towards securing a period of consolidation in European activity, and in seeking to persuade the European Commission to balance the risks, costs and benefits of their proposals before putting them forward. I am glad to say that our approach was rewarded by the submission to the European Commission by its Advisory Committee on Safety Health and Hygiene of a programme with priority given to consolidation, and with attention drawn to implementation and enforcement measures.

The management of health and safety

The most important of the new European-based regulations has been the Management of Health and Safety Regulations introduced as part of the 'six-pack' but in fact devised as a framework for future European law on employee safety and health. Its most important provision establishes the principle that protective action must be based on an assessment of risk. This is essentially a management principle, entirely in accord with our own views that significant further improvements in standards depend on the better management of health and safety as well as attention to prioritisation and targeting of activity towards the significant risks.

It has always been my own conviction that concern for the management of the health and safety aspects of any business is an excellent 'way in' to the management of other aspects of production and personnel, demonstrating as it does a human concern on the part of top managers. It is in fact ground on which management and worker can meet uncontroversially. Its usefulness as a tool of quality management was further demonstrated by a remarkable document published by the Executive in the course of the year and referred to by the Director General in his foreword, on the financial costs of accidental events - generally not appreciated or recorded in balance sheets.

Reform and deregulation

Since 1974 we have made considerable progress in modernising and simplifying health and safety law. Many unnecessary requirements have been removed and new, goal-setting legislation has been introduced. In early 1993 this continuing work gained a new focus when the Government invited us, along with other major Departments and agencies, to review by April 1994 all the remaining legislation for which we are responsible. The review, on which we are being advised by seven industrial Task Groups, is examining whether there are burdens arising for business which are not offset by benefits and which could be eased without endangering necessary health and safety standards. We have also reviewed with Ministers our European strategy, so as to take full account of the deregulation initiative. We shall continue to challenge vigorously proposals that appear to us unduly prescriptive, not based on sound scientific and technical arguments, or likely to fail to bring benefits commensurate with the costs.

The bottom line

This report shows that the number of deaths from accidents at work has been reduced to the lowest on record. The improvement in the rate of fatalities is larger than would be expected simply as a result of changing patterns of employment. However, there has been no improvement in the non-fatal injury rate which, after allowing for changes in employment, has remained at around the same level since the start of the current series in 1986/87. We can therefore derive little comfort from these figures, albeit that they appear to indicate a better record than in most other European countries.

Finally, I should like to record my great appreciation for all the help and support I have received over the past ten years from all the Commissioners who have served with me, from members of the Executive and the staff of HSE. During my time as Chairman, the Health and Safety Commission has taken on a variety of important new tasks. There has been a significant growth of EC activity on health and safety matters and increasing public and international interest. These are challenging times for the Health and Safety Commission and its new Chairman and I wish them well in the difficult tasks which face them in the coming years.

Sir John Cullen FEng PhD

DIRECTOR GENERAL'S FOREWORD

This has been a year, for HSE, of continued growth to meet the new responsibilities for offshore and railway safety transferred to us in 1990 and 1991; of adaptation to meet the need to implement a mass of new European-based legislation on health and safety; and of self examination in the light of developments in Government policy, not least the Prime Minister's renewed deregulation initiative.

It has been a difficult, but on the whole successful year. On our offshore and railway responsibilities, we have met every target set us ahead of time. There now exist the foundations of a new framework of offshore law meeting the recommendations, as recently as 1990, of the Cullen Inquiry, and Offshore Safety Division has been built up rapidly and has assumed its place as a new force not only in the UK but in the world offshore industry. The Railway Inspectorate has been revitalised and the Commission's proposals for a viable regulatory structure for a privatised railway system have been accepted by Ministers. Our Field Operations Division, though hampered during its short life by the need to redress a serious imbalance created by the part-replacement of a highly experienced inspector corps by a large body of talented but inexperienced recruits, has come of age. And the reorganisation we carried out two years ago of our Policy Divisions is proving successful. HSE, taken as a whole, was by the year end more dynamic, fuller of talent, and as determined to succeed in its work of maintaining and improving industrial safety standards in the UK, as at any time in its history.

I have referred to imperatives arising from Government policy. Two in particular have impinged on HSE. During the summer of 1992 the Government announced its renewed determination to identify the core of public services needing to be kept within the public sector, and to market test and contract out, or privatise those elements that on a value-for-money basis might best be carried on outside Government. The Health and Safety Commission took the view that this requirement could best be met by a comprehensive review of the regulatory operations of HSE rather than by some piecemeal exposure of activity to the market. They asked me to carry out that review, and I reported to them and they to Ministers in November 1992 that although there was no technical impediment to market testing any activity other than policy making, there would be important risks and drawbacks to set against any advantages of market testing the main operational arms of HSE. Such arguments do not necessarily apply to other sectors of our work. No decision has as yet been taken on the main conclusions of my review; and I proceeded during the spring of 1993 to carry out a further review of the scientific services provided by our Research and Laboratory Services Division on which we depend to enlarge our main stock in trade - knowledge of industrial hazard. This review was in progress at the end of the reporting year.

In 1993, the Government reinforced its efforts whenever possible to remove burdens on business, particularly small enterprises, through measures of deregulation. HSE was not a special target of this initiative, but we are of course a major regulatory body of very wide scope and influence on business. It so happened that the Government's initiative took place at the time of the introduction of a set of new European-based health and safety measures (the 'six-pack') which add up to the biggest development in health and safety law since the 1974 Act. We were therefore singled out for a great deal of public attention, and for some public criticism. At the request of Ministers, the Health and Safety Commission announced in February a comprehensive review of existing health and safety law with an aim to propose the removal of provisions not making a contribution proportionate to the costs they inflict. This review, which is involving businessmen and trades unionists, was also in progress at the end of the reporting year.

HSE often finds itself between a rock and a hard place, with criticism from some quarters of 'over-zealous' behaviour by inspectors, and from other quarters of lack of 'zeal', eg in pursuing individuals for health and safety offences. HSE inspectors come across many very hazardous activities and will and must act firmly to protect those engaged in them. But they are expected by the Executive to use considerable discretion in not intervening in unimportant matters and not standing on the letter of the law or guidance in pettifogging ways. In fact recent surveys make it clear that HSE inspectors continue to enjoy a high standing and regard throughout industry, and among those who actually meet them.

In addition to the progress made in the acceptance of our new responsibilities, significant steps have been taken towards stimulating an improvement in the way safety is managed throughout industry. Apart from the new Management of Health and Safety Regulations, which have clarified long-standing requirements that employers should assess the risks in their operations, much attention has been secured to techniques of risk assessment in determining action on major hazards and in deciding the value for money of new policies both within and well outside the area of industrial health and safety. Among last year's major achievements were a highly successful conference sponsored in London by HSE in conjunction with the European Community, OECD and the ILO; the revision and republication of the Executive's pathbreaking work *The tolerability of risk from nuclear power stations*; and the publication of a major new study on comparative risks in the transportation of hazardous materials which has stimulated a worldwide interest. One of the achievements in this area of which we are proudest is winning the European Commission's contract for devising a system for risk assessment of chemicals together with the appropriate guidance for the authorities implementing new European legislation.

A significant development has been the completion and publication by the Executive of the results of much recent research on the actual costs of industrial unsafety, and in particular, of five studies carried out in conjunction with different firms, of what accidents were actually costing them. Suffice it to say that all the firms engaged in the study were surprised at the extent of these costs, most of which were uninsured, did not appear in balance sheets, and represented a gross drag on their performance and profits. Much progress has also been made during the year in ascertaining and publicising the true (and considerable) extent of industrial ill health. I believe that the majority of employers attach more importance than they are often given credit for to the human side of safety precaution; it may be right now to give as much attention to the financial side.

Operations and results

During the year most of the inspectorates grew in size so as to absorb - sometimes retrospectively - the large number of new responsibilities acquired by HSE in recent years. As a consequence, net efficiency was reduced because of the 'dilution' of experience; - in the Factory Inspectorate, over 35% of inspectors have less than 5 years' experience and some 27% were undergoing preliminary training during the year. What has stood out has been the splendid quality of the new recruits, and the way they are standing up to their formidable training schedules and workloads. A high proportion have some previous industrial experience.

Finally, it is satisfactory to record signs that the courts are taking note of the importance of the health and safety offences that we bring before them, and are taking advantage of the latitude given them by the raising in 1992 of the maximum level of fines. HSE does not prosecute unless we are satisfied that a serious breakdown of reasonable precaution has taken or is taking place.

When we are so satisfied, we will bring before the courts either the firm or if the breakdown is clearly in our view attributable to her or him, any individual, director or worker who can properly and reasonably be accused. We have a statutory responsibility to enforce the law, and can only follow our policy of moderation and restraint on the basis that when we do act, the courts will register the full extent of the dereliction.

J D Rimington CB

PART I

Chapter 1 MAIN ACHIEVEMENTS AGAINST PRIORITIES

1.1   The Commission's published Plan of Work for 1992/93 and beyond set out its main priorities in Chapter 2. This chapter reports on achievement against those priorities, and on developments in certain areas which became priorities following publication of the plan.

1.2   Later chapters cover action in relation to particular hazards (Chapter 2) and industries (Chapter 3); and Chapter 4 reports on the management of the Health and Safety Executive. The report also includes the main points from HSC's Statistical Supplement, the full version of which is now published separately.

OFFSHORE SAFETY   *Priority: To secure the making of regulations to introduce a safety case regime offshore, implementing Lord Cullen's principal recommendation, and begin to translate the regulations into an effective implementing regime.*

1.3   The Offshore Installations (Safety Case) Regulations, which require operators and owners of offshore fixed and mobile installations to prepare a safety case for each installation and submit them to HSE for acceptance, were laid before Parliament on 27 November 1992

and came into force on 31 May 1993. Safety cases for existing installations must be submitted by 30 November 1993, with a transitional period until 30 November 1995 for HSE to assess safety cases and agree any necessary improvements with operators. Beyond this date it will be an offence to operate an offshore installation on the UK Continental Shelf without an accepted safety case. *A guide to the Offshore Installations (Safety Case) Regulations 1992* was published in November 1992.

1.4 The regulations require each safety case to demonstrate that:

*   management systems are adequate;

*   there are adequate arrangements for regular, independent audit of the systems;

*   hazards with the potential to cause major accidents have been identified; and

*   risks of major accidents have been evaluated and measures taken to reduce risks to people to the lowest level that is reasonably practicable. This should include demonstration of adequate provision for evacuation, escape and rescue of people, including temporary refuge where this is necessary.

1.5 The regulations also require advance notification to HSE of certain well operations and certain construction activities. Fuller details of activities on offshore safety are given in Chapter 3.

HSE's offshore inspectors examine a survival craft on Shell's Sean P Platform

INSPECTION, ADVICE AND ENFORCEMENT

Priority: To increase and broaden the impact of HSE's field force by better targeted action firmly based on local knowledge and priorities.

1.6   Last year's report outlined the conclusions of the Impact study which considered how inspector resource in HSE's Field Operations Division (FOD) could be used most effectively to produce improved control of risk. A key first step in implementing the recommendations has been the *development of new approaches to inspection* (as described in the following paragraphs). Evaluation of these approaches is also being developed to allow field staff to measure baseline health and safety standards in a target sector of industry and then to study the effects, over a period of time, of different contact techniques. Taken together with an analysis of the resource costs to HSE of particular approaches this should lead to better informed decisions about future inspection programmes.

1.7   Examples of initiatives underway include the following:

- inspectors in one region have developed a technique for involving directors of medium sized firms more directly in the control of health and safety risks, so that they accept responsibility for, and ownership of, the solutions. The effectiveness of this technique in smaller firms, in this case garages, is now being evaluated;

- in another region inspectors are tackling poor standards in the woodworking industry by combining the normal inspection programme with contact through seminars and distribution of informative newsletters to firms - again an evaluation is in hand.

1.8   The *range of inspection techniques* now in use is illustrated by the following examples:

- some large organisations in the construction and motor manufacturing sectors have been the subject of *central approaches* to evaluate their approach to management of health and safety. *Auditing techniques* are also being developed for use in inspection of the more hazardous plants;

- *seminars* have been used more widely, enabling advice and information to be given to groups of local business people. A total of nearly 500 attended one series of seven seminars. In another initiative, a *workshop was held for senior managers* to highlight key elements of health and safety management in their organisations. The participants were encouraged to draw up their own action plans for managing health and safety. In assessing the impact of these events, organisers will be looking for signs that employers have been stimulated to improve their control of workplace hazard;

- *local inspection campaigns* continued to be used as a way of concentrating inspection effort in a selected locality for a period spanning a few days to a week. Campaigns were typically supported by publicity to encourage greater awareness and preventive action. Often one of the main aims was to identify and visit firms not known to HSE. Some campaigns were used to measure the effect of innovatory methods and approaches, for example, whether advance notification of visits accompanied by guidance material prompted remedial action before inspections took place. In one instance, advance notification caused neighbouring firms on an industrial estate to provide mutual self-help by sharing knowledge and experience of health and safety matters.

1.9   Work has continued to explore the use of intermediary organisations such as Training and Enterprise Councils, trade unions and trade associations in helping to take forward HSE objectives. A number of examples of industry or sector specific initiatives are included in Chapters 2 and 3.

1.10 The pilot scheme in which specially trained administrative staff were used to update the database of registered premises has now been converted to a permanent arrangement with staff, known as *workplace contact officers*, appointed in all areas. Their main functions include identification of new workplaces, including existing ones previously unknown to HSE, and checking the continuing existence of registered firms not visited for a long time. They promote awareness by distributing information packs.

Enforcement

1.11 In line with the recommendations of the Impact Report there has been a *shift in emphasis and approach*. In particular, in order to tackle root causes rather than just the symptoms of unsafe and unhealthy conditions, inspectors are now much more frequently considering companies' arrangements for the management of health and safety, backed up by enforcement action in appropriate circumstances. Where the circumstances warrant it, HSE will consider prosecution of senior members of management. It is, however, unlikely that there will be a rapid rise in the number of such prosecutions since it is generally more difficult to collect evidence to prosecute an individual than a company. And it is important, if the confidence of management as a whole is to be retained, that any such prosecution be capable of being widely recognised as deserved.

1.12 These new approaches require new techniques and procedures such as tape recording interviews and leading expert evidence in relation to management matters. Work has also been needed to establish how enforcement notices may best be drafted on such subjects.

Penalties

1.13 This was the first full year of the operation of the new penalties brought in in 1992. The use magistrates have made of them demonstrate that these penalties were needed. In magistrates' courts and sheriffs' courts in Scotland the average fine rose from £587 to £942; however almost all of this rise is accounted for by the English and Welsh courts. Examples of the use of high fines include:

- Leicester magistrates fined Alexandra Stone Company, a construction firm, £18 000 after an employee died from falling through a roof;

- Hull magistrates fined William Jackson and Son, a bakery, £17 000 after an employee sustained three broken fingers and cuts to his arm when it was trapped in a bread roll making machine.

With the use of the higher penalties the average in all courts rose from £1181 to £1384.

1.14 On 26 June 1992, following a conviction for non-compliance with a Prohibition Notice in her court, the Recorder at Lewes Crown Court disqualified a director of Chapman Chalk Supplies, a chalk extraction company, from acting as a director for two years. This decision was important as it confirmed HSC/E's view that the 'management' of a company includes the management of health and safety and that, therefore, a conviction for an indictable health and safety offence opens a director up to disqualification under section 2 of the Company Directors Disqualification Act 1986.

Developments in the local authority sector

1.15 The '*lead authority*' pilot scheme began in autumn 1992, involving five volunteer large companies and the relevant local authorities. The scheme builds on work done in HSE on central approaches to large companies (see paragraph 1.8 above) and aims to improve consistency of treatment by local authorities enforcing health and safety among the outlets of national or regional companies. Under the pilot a safety management review will be completed by summer 1993 and the recommendations communicated to all local authorities with outlets of the companies in their area. Each lead authority will then act as a link between the company and other local authorities. They will provide information, identify issues of sectoral or national consequence and generally inform the inspection and enforcement process of local authorities in relation to their partner company.

1.16 The pilots will be evaluated in the coming year.

IMPLEMENTATION OF FRAMEWORK AND ASSOCIATED DIRECTIVES

Priority: To implement the Framework Directive, its associated 'daughter' directives and other European legislation in a manner consistent with UK law and practice and to ensure that new law is comprehensible to those affected by it.

1.17 The European Community's Health and Safety Framework Directive sets out general principles for establishing minimum health and safety requirements in the EC. Implementation was required by 31 December 1992, together with six closely associated directives dealing with:

- equipment safety;

- workplace conditions;

- manual handling of loads;

4

- personal protective equipment;

- use of display screens; and

- temporary workers.

1.18 In 1991/92 HSC published proposals for implementing these directives and in 1992/93 the draft regulations and associated Advisory Codes of Practice (ACoPs) and guidance were revised in the light of comments made, before being put to Employment Department Ministers for approval. The regulations were laid before Parliament and the ACoPs and guidance were published by December 1992. The regulations took effect on 1 January 1993.

1.19 The aim throughout was to fit the new regulations into the legal framework established by the HSW Act and to continue to reform the legislation which pre-dates it. In doing so, HSE was aware of the need to maintain or improve existing standards; to keep employers fully informed about what the new regulations mean for them; and to avoid undue burdens on business.

1.20 To this end, HSE developed a ***promotional and educational strategy*** designed to assist understanding of the new requirements. This included two 'early warning' leaflets which gave basic guidance and explained how to obtain more detailed information; and an extensive press advertising campaign to bring the new regulations to the attention of employers and the public generally. In addition, HSE staff gave many presentations and seminars to a variety of organisations at both national and local level, to help raise awareness and understanding. Field staff made particular efforts to target smaller firms who often require more guidance. HSE has also issued more specific guidance on aspects of the new regulations, and more is being prepared.

1.21 Inevitably some employers seem to have gained the impression that the regulations place a greater burden upon them than is actually the case. In particular, some ***consultants*** have misled employers about the implications of the new legislation. HSE issued warnings about consultants who appeared to be misinterpreting the regulations in order to generate business, and produced a leaflet *Selecting a health and safety consultancy,* which aims to help smaller businesses decide if they need help from consultants and, if so, how to get value for money.

1.22 HSE staff received appropriate training in the new legislation. Over 1100 people were trained and staff with enforcement responsibility for the legislation were given priority. Nominated local authority representatives were trained alongside HSE inspectors, and in addition, HSE Area staff trained many LA inspectors on an individual basis.

1.23 HSE's ***enforcement*** policy on the new regulations was clearly spelled out before the regulations came into effect. Inspectors' approach has been to promote awareness of the regulations and the duties they place on employers. They have pointed employers in the direction of sources of advice and guidance as necessary. HSE made clear that in the early stages of implementation formal enforcement would only be likely if:

- the risks to health and safety are evident and immediate; or

- what needs to be done is not new (ie existing duties have been transposed into the new legislation); or

- employers appear deliberately obdurate and unwilling to recognise their responsibilities to ensure the long term health, safety and welfare of employees and others affected by their activities.

Local authorities were encouraged by HELA to adopt the same approach to the enforcement of these regulations.

INTERNATIONAL LAW AND STANDARDS MAKING

Priority: Against the background of the increasing internationalisation of law and standards making in health and safety and environmental matters, to maximise UK influence and to secure the application of UK approaches.

1.24 The Plan of Work identified completion of the Single Market and Social Action Programmes by the end of 1992 as the main forces combining to produce a high level of EC activity. During this period the European Year of Health and Safety (see paragraphs 1.89-1.95 below) and the UK Presidency of the Council of Ministers together provided an unequalled opportunity for HSC/E to exert considerable influence over outcomes covering a range of important issues.

1.25 During the UK Presidency, HSC/E contributed fully to supporting the aims and priorities set by Employment Ministers and their colleagues in other Departments. Throughout negotiations on a range of health and safety proposals the UK made substantial and constructive contributions in the development and shaping of legislation with the firm aim of securing outcomes satisfactory to the UK government and industry.

1.26 The Presidency provided a number of opportunities to promote a *more consistent approach to the enforcement of EC legislation* by all Member States. These included:

- discussion at the EC Senior Labour Inspectors' Committee on how common principles of health and safety inspection could be developed across the Community. This important work is continuing;

- emphasis in the conclusions of the Labour and Social Affairs Council on the need for the Community to strengthen commitment to more effective implementation and enforcement of EC legislation, including directives on health and safety. The Council specifically welcomed the work of the Senior Labour Inspectors in this connection;

- a major conference on enforcement run by HSE, in conjunction with the Institution of Environmental Health Officers, was attended by all authorities with responsibility for health and safety enforcement in Europe and the EC labour inspectorates.

1.27 Looking beyond 1992, the UK argued for a period of consolidation and for implementation and enforcement, risk assessment, attention to cost-benefit assessment and regulations which set goals rather than prescribe detailed requirements, in the tripartite group established by the European Commission to advise on its *future work on health and safety*. A good many of these themes were reflected in recommendations put to the European Commission by the tripartite Luxembourg Advisory Committee in February 1992. The Luxembourg Advisory Committee was set up in 1974 to assist the EC in the preparation and implementation of health and safety activities and is made up of representatives from Member States, including workers and employers.

1.28 There was considerable progress in HSE's *wider international work*. In particular:

- in nuclear safety, HSE continued to promote the development of high world-wide safety

Topping out of Sizewell B

standards mainly through the International Atomic Energy Agency, and particularly through the Agency's proposed Nuclear Safety Convention. With the possibility that HSE may be asked to license a reactor of overseas design for operation in the UK, HSE has continued exchanges with foreign regulators with the aim of reaching a common understanding of regulatory philosophies and standards applied in reactor design.

- HSE also continued to develop effective international relationships in offshore safety. This has included annual meetings with representatives of North Sea states within the North Sea Offshore Authorities Forum and representation on working groups examining offshore safety training and legislative requirements for mobile drilling units. A number of regulatory authorities have expressed interest in the UK safety case regime.

1.29 HSE vigorously pursued the policy described in the plan as to the *OECD Existing Substances programme*. In conjunction with DoE, UK work on the Phase 1 was completed and this was well received by OECD members in February 1993. HSE strongly supported moves to co-ordinate the work of the OECD programme with work arising from the EC Regulation on Existing Substances. This will avoid duplication of effort by Member States.

1.30 The conclusions from the UN conference on Environment and Development in Rio de Janeiro in June 1992 were encouraging and in line with HSC's views on *chemical risk assessment and management*. An important outcome in this area was a commitment by the signatories to work toward a globally harmonised scheme for classification and labelling of dangerous substances by the year 2000. This work will be co-ordinated by the International Programme on Chemical Safety (IPCS). The UK is represented on the IPCS Management Committee which will plan and oversee the activity.

RISK ASSESSMENT

Priority: To develop further the use of risk assessment as a tool for prioritising action to reduce risk.

1.31 The Government's renewed initiative on deregulation (see paragraphs 1.99-1.101 below) has underlined the importance of proportioning action to risk, bringing increased interest across Whitehall in the approaches HSE has long promoted in its regulatory and enforcement activities. HSE's efforts were reinforced by the establishment of its Risk Assessment Policy Unit in autumn 1992 with the aim of promoting a coherent and consistent approach within HSE and in national and international fora. The unit provides the secretariat for an Interdepartmental Liaison Group on Risk Assessment (ILGRA), chaired by HSE's Director of Strategy and General Division. ILGRA has been given the task of producing a report on the use and application of risk assessment within Whitehall.

1.32 The following examples illustrate the value of risk assessment in policy making:

- with the use of risk assessment in advising local planning authorities on the risk to people in the vicinity of major hazards, large areas formerly affected by planning blight have been released for development; and

- a report by Mr Brian Appleton, commissioned by HSE to investigate relative risks of different action following fire or security alerts on London Underground, demonstrated how an all-risk assessment approach could better inform priorities for safety expenditure. At the time of his study fire represented only 3% of remaining risk on the underground but accounted for 80% of safety expenditure.

1.33 HSE has made a considerable effort to promote *understanding of risk assessment by employers*. In particular it has sought to publicise, and put in perspective, the new risk assessment requirements of the regulations implementing the EC Framework and associated directives. A video on risk assessment, targeted at small firms, was produced in collaboration with the Engineering Employers Federation. Inspectors have emphasised the common sense and practical nature of the risk assessment process. In particular, they have explained that it is not necessary to prepare massive paper documentation on risk assessments and that most employers should be able to tackle this work satisfactorily without recourse to using health and safety consultants.

1.34 HSE has continued to influence the *EC and international developments*. In October 1992 more than 300 delegates attended an *international conference on risk assessment* in London. The conference was co-sponsored by the HSC, EC, ILO, OECD and WHO. The conference, aimed at promoting the use of risk assessment and achieving greater coherence and consistency in its use, was addressed by speakers from a wide range of countries, including Eastern Europe. The spectrum of risk interests covered was very wide ranging, from well established technologies to emerging ones.

1.35 HSE has successfully promoted its approach to risk assessment in a number of specific areas of EC work:

- the introduction of risk assessment into the EC directive concerning new chemical substances and the EC regulation on existing chemical substances represents a significant step forward in the use of this technique in international fora. The philosophy that chemicals should be assessed as to their overall risks to man and the environment is now firmly established in the EC and OECD. HSE has been awarded a major contract to supply the technical guidance on the methodology to underpin this assessment;

- HSE is helping develop EC guidance on the general principles of risk assessment underlying the Health and Safety Framework Directive and their application by employers. This could facilitate the task of producing a more even application of the framework and associated directives in the Community.

MANAGEMENT OF HEALTH AND SAFETY

1.36 The importance of an effective system of managing risks to health and safety has been demonstrated in recent years by the management deficiencies which contributed to a number of disasters such as Piper Alpha, Chernobyl, Zeebrugge, Kings Cross and Clapham Junction. At the other end of the scale, there is growing evidence to indicate the costs to employers, and to the individuals affected, of minor accidents arising from deficiencies in basic management procedures. For these reasons recent HSC Plans of Work have given a high priority to a variety of measures aimed at improving standards of health and safety management.

Priority: To sustain and improve the ability of employers and others in the health and safety system to manage risk safely and where appropriate to improve the professionalism applied to health and safety matters, and the health and safety awareness of managers, including an awareness of the costs of neglecting health and safety.

Recent legislation

1.37 The ***Management of Health and Safety at Work Regulations 1992*** provide legislative support to an effective approach to managing health and safety in all aspects of work. These regulations came into force on 1 January 1993 and help to implement the EC Framework Directive (see paragraphs 1.17-1.23 above). They require employers to:

- assess workplace risks and act upon the findings;

- have effective arrangements for planning, organising, controlling, monitoring, and reviewing health and safety measures;

- have competent assistance (either from inside or outside the organisation) in carrying out health and safety measures;

- provide health surveillance where necessary;

- have effective emergency procedures;

- provide employees with adequate training and information on health and safety issues; and

- co-operate with employers whose employees are sharing the same work site.

The risks presented by poor housekeeping are highlighted at an Area Office open day

1.38 Several other legislative initiatives on particular sectors are contributing towards the aim of improving the ability of employers and others to manage risks to health and safety effectively. These include: regulations to introduce a safety case regime offshore; preparation of revised Construction (Design and Management) Regulations; and the mining legislation renewal programme, all of which are referred to in more detail in Chapter 3 of this report.

Cost benefits of effective management

1.39 HSE has also promoted the importance of the effective management of health and safety through its publications. For example, *The costs of accidents at work* was published in early 1993. It reports on collaborative studies by HSE's Accident Prevention Advisory Unit (APAU) with organisations in five different employment sectors. The studies recorded and quantified the costs arising from accidents during periods ranging between 13 to 18 weeks. The research costed not just accidents involving injuries, but also those involving damage, disruption and production losses.

1.40 For the companies concerned, depending on the parameters chosen in different cases, the costs represented:

- 37% of annualised profits;

- 8.5% of turnover;

- 5% of operating costs;

- 1.4% of turnover;

- the equivalent of closing down the process for one day a week.

1.41 Only a small proportion of the costs were covered by insurance. The uninsured costs were between 8 and 36 times greater than the cost of insurance premium paid at the time of the studies. Costs of this magnitude demonstrate the financial imperative to reduce accidents. APAU is currently developing the work further to enable smaller organisations to use the costs methodology described in the publication.

Audit of management of health and safety and quality management

1.42 APAU continued its programme of audits of the management of health and safety and six were undertaken during the year in a range of employment sectors including manufacturing, chemicals and leisure. In addition APAU provided advice to a number of organisations on ways of improving their existing arrangements for managing health and safety.

1.43 Inspectors have continued to place emphasis on management systems during their inspection and investigations, encouraging organisations to adopt the approach set out in *Successful health and safety management,* an approach very much in line with the philosophy behind BS5750.

Contribution of safety representatives

1.44 HSE has also been considering how the valuable contributions made by safety representatives to improving the management of health and safety can be enhanced. The Management of Health and Safety at Work Regulations amended the Safety Representatives and Safety Committees Regulations 1977 by specifying matters on which employers are required to consult safety representatives. A research project to develop improved guidance to promote the effectiveness of safety representatives and safety committees is nearing completion. The research was commissioned to fill a gap in HSC/E's existing guidance for safety representatives. The current 'brown booklet', though helpful in setting out the legal framework, provides little in the way of practical guidance. The results of this project may also have some application to current work on developing a self-teaching package for managers and workers' representatives. Progress on the separate review of safety representatives and committees offshore is described at paragraph 3.11.

1.45 In considering the effectiveness of safety representatives, HSE recognises that good communications and mutual understanding represent a sound starting point. Developments during the year included the Open Days held at most area offices during Workplace Health and Safety Week in November.

Health and safety training

1.46 HSE has continued to forge links with Lead Bodies which are developing standards of competence to ensure vocational qualifications based on them adequately cover health and safety. The Occupational Health and Safety Lead Body (OHSLB) is developing standards of competence for occupational health and safety practitioners with the active help of many practitioners and their professional and awarding bodies.

1.47 The Management of Health and Safety at Work Regulations have made more explicit the employer's duty to provide adequate health and safety training. A leaflet, *Train to survive*, was published during the European Year of Safety, Hygiene and Health at Work (EYSHH) Workplace Week to help them with this.

1.48 The ***training of managers*** is particularly important. Building on its earlier publication *Successful health and safety management*, HSE's Accident Prevention Advisory Unit (APAU) has been developing guidance for trainers on the health and safety competences required by managers. APAU has also continued to participate in the work of the Lead Body for quality management organised by the Management Charter Initiative (MCI) to ensure proper account is taken of health and safety.

1.49 Many firms are realising that health and safety training makes good business sense and can see the human and financial benefits which accrue from it. This was evident from the response (over 100 entries) to HSC's sponsorship of a special award under the Employment Department's ***National Training Awards competition*** to mark the European Year of Safety, Hygiene and Health Protection at Work.

Small businesses and the self employed

1.50 HSE devotes substantial effort to providing simple direct guidance aimed at smaller businesses and the self-employed where there is often no awareness of the importance of health and safety and of the measures needed to protect workers and the public. Initiatives during 1992/3 included:

- a free leaflet, *101 tips to a safer business*. This was developed by a secondee from a Chamber of Commerce and gave simple practical tips on how to run a small business more safely;

- a free leaflet, *Five steps to successful health and safety management*. This is a shorter version of APAU's publication *Successful health and safety management;*

- a video *Whose risk is it anyway*, designed to help small business owners and managers adopt a practical and effective approach to risk assessment;

- a free leaflet *Selecting a health and safety consultancy*, aimed at helping smaller businesses decide if they need help from consultants and, if so, how to get value for money.

1.51 To promote wider awareness of health and safety in small firms, HSE took steps to draw this material to the attention of a range of intermediary bodies - Training and Enterprise Councils (TECs), Local Enterprise Companies (LECs), Local Enterprise Agencies (LEAs), Chambers of Commerce etc - who work with small firms.

OCCUPATIONAL HEALTH *Priority: To establish the key points of attack in improving occupational health and identifying the extent of occupational ill health, and to exploit linkages between occupational health and 'Health of the Nation' initiative.*

1.52 New evidence of the scale of damage done by work to people's health now available - over two million cases in 1990 (estimated from the Labour Force Survey), and 1 in 20 GP consultations in the working age population are for work-related conditions - confirms the need signalled by HSC in recent years for more effective action to protect health.

1.53 During the year HSE took stock of its own efforts - policy, operations and technical, scientific and epidemiological intelligence activities - in relation to each major class of occupational health risk. The need for these reviews was identified following a progressive extension over the last 15 years of legislative controls on health risks from chemical, biological and physical agents, as a result in large part of EC and international activity, and also in the wake of new EC-led requirements for protection from poorly designed or organised work, in new management, display screen work and manual handling regulations.

1.54 The *reviews*, prepared for the end of the year, were designed to assess the adequacy of available information and the effectiveness of past and current activities by HSE, industry and others. They will lead to a programme of future action to include means of helping employers translate broad legal requirements into sensible practical steps to protect health. The conclusions will form the basis of HSC plans of action on health for 1994/5 and beyond.

1.55 Against the background of the new requirements in the Management of Health and Safety at Work Regulations for employers to appoint competent assistance, HSE commissioned a study to assess *employers' use of occupational health advisers* and their action on occupational health and health promotion. It found that:

• half the workforce is in establishments using health professionals;

• use of occupational hygienists has grown significantly since 1976;

• most (65%) private sector employers take action to protect workers' health;

• health hazards most commonly recognised were manual handling, chemicals, VDU work and dust/fumes.

1.56 Industry continues to seek advice on developing occupational health provision. EMAS gave over 100 presentations on this topic during the year.

1.57 Improving *links with the primary health care sector* has been a longstanding objective and with European Year of Health and Safety funding HSE launched a free handbook for family doctors and other health care professionals. *Your patients and their work* aims to raise doctors' interest in work aspects of patients' ill health and provides advice on common problems. Accompanied by a patients' leaflet to help doctors diagnose occupational illness, the booklet was distributed nationwide and promoted by EMAS staff on visits to general practices.

1.58 To maximise the impact of HSC/E's and industry's investment in preventing ill health, good *information* - on the pattern and severity as well as the scale of disease and damage - is an essential basis for determining priorities. HSE expanded its range of data sources by establishing a reporting scheme following a pilot for dermatitis (Epiderm) which makes use of consultant dermatologist expertise. Pilot recording schemes for urothelial tumours and pesticide related ill health ran throughout the year. The response rate for SWORD (Surveillance of Work Related and Occupational Respiratory Disease) has been increased so that over 3500 cases of work related lung disease are seen.

1.59 **Research projects** supported included a critical review of literature on stress in response to growing interest in this area of ill health and a major study of the relationship of asthma and chronic bronchitis with occupation.

1.60 Recognition of the workplace as an important setting for action to promote healthy lifestyles is central to the Government's major initiative on health launched in June 1992, 'Health of the Nation'. HSE is contributing expertise in ill health prevention in the workplace, through the Health Secretary's Wider Health Working Group, through task forces and sub-groups concerned with the workplace, accidents and smoking, and through advice from the HSC's Health Services Advisory Committee to help the NHS implement a new health at work programme.

RAILWAYS   *Priority: To develop HSE's capacity, through the Railway Inspectorate, to deal with changes in the industry and increasing railway activity; and to secure improvements in railway safety.*

1.61 There was consultation during the year, with the Departments of Employment and Transport, to identify a realistic level of resource to meet both HSE's existing railway safety commitments; changes consequent on HSE's advice on the safety aspects of the Government's liberalisation and privatisation proposals; and the added responsibilities imposed by the Transport and Works Act 1992.

A train crashed into a platform at Maidstone East causing massive damage and disruption

1.62 Railway Inspectorate staff will be increased in 1993/94 by approximately 30% over the previous year. There is a further planned increase of up to 45% over existing levels during the two-year period 1994/96 when the privatisation programme is likely to be at its height. Commensurate increases for the Safety Policy Division have already been implemented to enable HSE to advise the Secretary of State for Transport on the safety implications of the liberalisation and privatisation policies (see paragraph 1.64 below).

1.63 Further details of the work of the Railway Inspectorate are set out in Chapter 3.

Liberalisation and privatisation of British Rail

1.64 As the year progressed, it became clear that a priority task for the Commission was to advise Ministers on changes required to the regulatory framework in the light of Government proposals for the liberalisation and privatisation of British Rail. The Health and Safety Commission provided detailed comprehensive advice and guidance to Ministers concerning the safety implications of the liberalisation and privatisation programme. Their recommendations were contained in a report *Ensuring safety on British Railways*, published by the Department of Transport in January 1993. All recommendations were accepted by the Government and endorsed by British Rail.

1.65 The report sets out a sound basis for a workable regime to ensure safety standards are maintained under privatisation of the railways, and clearly establishes the central role of HSE as the regulatory authority for all aspects of railway safety.

1.66 Work has begun on developing an enhanced health and safety regime, and new regulations under HSWA will, inter alia:

- require all new rail undertakings to produce a *railway safety case* which must be validated by a second party and implemented;

- endorse clear *standards for selection and competence of safety critical staff;* and

- provide sufficient *controls on the transport of all categories of dangerous substances.*

ENVIRONMENT   *Priority: To work with the Environment Departments towards consistency in policy and local action as between health and safety of people and protection of the natural environment.*

1.67 As noted in previous reports, a large proportion of polluting agents in the environment are produced by industrial undertakings which are regulated both by HSE and by the environmental regulatory authorities for different but closely related purposes. There has continued to be a strong emphasis on environmental issues in domestic, European and international fora during the year and it remains important that the regulatory effort of the various enforcing authorities is consistent and properly coordinated, achieving the most cost-effective and least burdensome approach.

1.68 During the year HSE and DoE have reviewed and begun to streamline their *policy links*, to enable both to become more jointly responsive to the increasing number of strategic issues which affect health, safety and environmental protection.

1.69 In terms of **operational liaison**, the Memorandum of Understanding between HSE and **Her Majesty's Inspectorate of Pollution** (HMIP) has continued to provide an effective framework for operations at national and local level; it has helped to ensure effective co-ordination of enforcement as the new regime of integrated pollution control under the Environmental Protection Act has become further established.

1.70 HSE's Field Operations Division has contributed to the development of detailed guidance being prepared by HMIP and DoE on the processes to be subject to integrated and air pollution control, and to the consideration of applications for authorisations to operate such processes.

1.71 In autumn 1992, HSE and the **National Rivers Authority** (which, like HMIP, is to form part of the new Environment Agency) agreed an operational Memorandum of Understanding, setting out appropriate liaison arrangements in areas of mutual interest.

INFORMATION AND STATISTICS

Priority: To improve the network of information and statistics available to help the Health and Safety Commission, HSE and local authorities interpret the state of worker safety and health in order better to prioritise and target the activities of HSE and local authorities and judge their impact.

1.72 Proposals to simplify the RIDDOR injury reporting requirements, the reporting procedures, and to enhance the capture of data about ill health were developed during the year. However, recent developments in the legislative programmes concerning the offshore oil and railway industries have presented an opportunity to prepare a single set of reporting regulations applying to all employers. A consultative document on this basis will be issued shortly.

1.73 A special health and safety supplement to the 1990 Labour Force Survey provided useful new evidence about the scale of work-related accidents and ill health. The detailed results on injuries were published in the Employment Gazette for December 1992 and draw particular attention to the relative risks in small and large workplaces, different occupations and between industries. Paragraph 1.58 refers to other improvements in data on ill health.

1.74 Paragraphs 1.39-1.41 referred to the results of case studies on the **cost of accidents at work**. These have been combined with data from the health and safety trailer to the 1990 Labour Force Survey by HSE economists to provide estimates of the total cost of workplace accidents (whether or not they cause injuries) and work-related ill health to employers, the affected individuals and their families and the country as a whole. These estimates reveal that:

- workplace accidents and work-related ill health **costs individuals and their families** around £1 billion a year (in 1990 prices) in reduced incomes and additional expenditures. The total costs, allowing for the further cost of pain, grief and suffering, is almost £5 billion a year, net of compensation;

- workplace accidents and work-related ill health **costs employers** between £4 billion and £9 billion a year, equivalent to between 5% and 10% of all UK industrial companies' gross trading profits or between £170 and £360 per person employed;

- the **total cost to society** as a whole is between £11 billion and £16 billion a year, equivalent to between 2% and 3% of total gross domestic product. Work-related illness accounts for between £4 and £5 billion of this cost.

1.75 The Health and Safety Executive/Local Authority Enforcement Liaison Committee (HELA) produces an annual report. It contains detailed accident statistics and information about *local authority enforcement activity and trends*. These data enable local authorities to target their resources to areas of greatest risk. Statistics published in 1992, for example, included special features on the retail and hotel and catering industries. New report forms were developed during 1992 which will improve the scope and effectiveness of the data in HELA's annual report for 1993/94 and subsequent years.

1.76 Following the creation of a new Research Strategy Unit (see Chapter 4) HSE's Research Committee is taking a more strategic role and preparing a statement on *HSE's research strategy*. Cross-divisional groups have been established to identify research needs in particular subjects and papers from a number of these subject research groups have informed the Research Committee's consideration of the overall balance of the research programme.

1.77 *Intelligence on technological issues* is of central importance in enabling HSE to direct its efforts more effectively. Initiatives taken during the year included:

* a review of HSE's strategy for training in the area of *safety related control systems* and work with the Institution of Electrical Engineers on the development of a Diploma and MSc course on safety-related systems; and

* organisation of a *conference* on chemical carcinogens, and a major role in others, including the British Occupational Hygiene Society Annual Conference at which HSE radiation and biosafety specialists presented papers.

1.78 Progress on the way handling other types of information is being improved, as part of HSE's second five-year *Information Strategy*, including the FOCUS project, is described in Chapter 4.

Priority: In conformity with the Citizen's Charter initiative, to improve the way in which various parts of HSE deal with the public.

1.79 A review which reported in late 1992 on HSE's contacts with the citizen suggested a number of improvements to systems for dealing with the public. Its main recommendations were implemented during 1992/93.

1.80 A key starting point was to carry out late in 1991/92 a *national census of levels of contact with the public*, and to measure response times to their enquiries. Results were analysed early in 1992/93 and showed that, during a typical two-week period, around 20 000 enquiries were received from employers, employees and the general public (equivalent to some 500 000 enquiries a year). Over 70% of enquiries to HSE's area offices were dealt with on the day they were received. Other, more complicated enquiries inevitably take longer to respond to. Nevertheless, results showed that over 90% of all enquiries were answered within ten working days. HSE's target is to respond to all enquiries, or to let the inquirer know what is being done, within 10 working days. This target has been published in two free booklets (see paragraph 1.84 below) and monitoring of it will continue. A regular annual rolling census programme started during 1992/93.

1.81 During the year a pilot survey was undertaken to find out whether a sample of those who contact HSE were satisfied with the way in which their enquiries had been handled. This showed that, of respondents who contacted area offices, 80% were satisfied with HSE's action on that occasion and 94% thought that HSE Field Operations Division's action generally was 'excellent' or 'very good'. The *satisfaction survey* will be repeated at the end of the current rolling census programme.

1.82 Measures taken during the year to enhance customer access included extended opening hours for HSE's Information Centres; the setting up of dedicated telephone lines to order HSE's publications; standardisation and extension of area office opening hours; and the provision of an answerphone service to give out of hours contact points for urgent messages.

1.83 The review of contacts also recommended that HSE staff in regular contact with the public should give their names on the telephone, wear name badges, or show their warrants or give out business cards when they visit. This policy has now been implemented. Guidance has also been issued to HSE inspectors on procedure during and following operational visits involving contact with private individuals.

1.84 HSE is a complex organisation with wide ranging responsibilities and people wishing to contact HSE sometimes need guidance to clarify what HSE can, and cannot do, how to get in touch, and how to complain if dissatisfied with HSE's response. To meet this need HSE published two free booklets during the year which cover these issues. The first, *The Health and Safety Executive and You*, aimed primarily at the general public, was published in September. The second, *The Health and Safety Executive - working with employers*, was published in November. Both booklets publicised HSE's aim of responding to enquiries, or to letting the inquirer know what is being done, within 10 working days. The demand for both booklets has been high, with over 116 000 copies issued by the end of the year.

Disclosure of information

1.85 HSC/E has continued to respond positively and constructively to moves towards greater openness with health and safety information while seeking to ensure that such moves do not endanger their primary functions of protecting health and safety. There were a number of developments during the year which led to greater openness.

1.86 Under the Environmental Information Regulations 1992, which implement the *EC directive on freedom of access to information relating to the environment*, and which came into force on 31 December 1992, HSC/E will make environmental information available on request in those areas where it has environmental responsibilities. These areas are pesticides, new substances, genetically modified organisms, control of industrial major accident hazards, onshore and cross country pipelines and polychlorinated biphenyls and polychlorinated terphenyls. The regulations exempt certain types of information from disclosure (eg information affecting national or public security, commercial confidentiality, personal privacy or that which was voluntarily supplied).

1.87 In January 1993 HSE began a pilot exercise at its two Area Offices in Scotland in *making details of inspection reports publicly available on request.* In most cases this means the letter written by the inspector to the employees at the inspected premises following the inspection, together with a copy of any enforcement notice or other enforcement action. The pilot exercise is intended to last for six months at the end of which it will be fully evaluated. In a similar exercise the Nuclear Safety Division is making quarterly reports on the Hunterston B nuclear site available to the local liaison committee.

1.88 On 1 January 1992 the *Public Information for Radiation Emergencies Regulations 1992* came into force. They implement Directive 89/618/Euratom and require employers and the self-employed conducting an undertaking where a radiation emergency **is r**easonably foreseeable to make certain prior information available to everyone in the area likely to be affected and also to make the information publicly available. In addition, the regulations require arrangements for the supply of information during an emergency to be made.

Priority: To take full advantage of the European Year of Safety, Hygiene and Health Protection at Work to focus attention on health, safety and hygiene in the workplace and on the importance of the European dimension.

1.89 The European Year provided a major opportunity to raise awareness, impart knowledge and stimulate action to improve health and safety standards at workplace level. Small firms were a priority and the economic benefits of good health and safety practices were emphasised. The UK held the Presidency of the Council in the second half of 1992 and the European Year and Presidency special events programmes complemented and reinforced each other.

1.90 HSE supported *publicity for the Year* through an information pack which went out to over 11 500 people, high profile launches throughout the country, and press conferences, press releases and speeches.

1.91 The UK calendar of events featured over 500 national and local events organised by around 250 different bodies. The UK's total share of EC funding was nearly one million ECU. This was allocated to 108 practical initiatives which were likely to have some lasting impact at workplace level. Over 80% were targeted at small firms and 60% at young trainees.

1.92 The UK's first *Workplace Health and Safety Week* ran from 23-27 November 1992. It was designed to provide a focal point for the Year's activities and aimed to stimulate practical action in the workplace. Launched by Sir Jimmy Savile, it was supported by an action pack which was taken up by 100 000 workplaces throughout the country. HSE Area Offices held successful open days for employers and trade union safety representatives.

1.93 In addition to the major European conferences on the enforcement of health and safety legislation (see paragraph 1.26) and on risk assessment (paragraph 1.34) other *major events* included an international mining symposium (see paragraph 3.66), and a conference and exhibition on the Year's four themes (Eurosafe 93).

1.94 The Year provided a focus for existing initiatives and a stimulus for new ones. Participation extended beyond safety specialists and those usually reached by the enforcement authorities. The *involvement of intermediary organisations* (eg Training and Enterprise Councils and sectoral employer organisations) was particularly welcome. A number of initiatives helped local health and safety interests to establish links and work together. Indications that initiatives and information had reached the small firms sector and stimulated action were especially encouraging.

1.95 Some initiatives lasted well beyond the Year and further HSE campaigns are reinforcing its main messages. Reactions to the Workplace Week were very positive and over a quarter of respondents said it had prompted them to take measures which made an impact on working practices and conditions, eg increased wearing of personal protective equipment, identification

Sir Jimmy Savile talks to the press about Workplace Health and Safety Week

and removal of hazards, development or revision of safety policies. Some 98% of respondents said they would take part in a similar initiative in the future. A further Workplace Health and Safety Week is being considered as a means of maintaining the momentum generated by the Year in workplaces throughout the country.

ADDITIONAL PRIORITIES

1.96 Since the 1992/93 Plan of Work was published, there have been developments in Government policy - on rail and coal privatisation and on deregulation - which have created new priority tasks for the Commission and HSE. Work on the safety implications of rail privatisation was described in paragraphs 1.64-1.66: action in response to the other new priorities is described below.

FUTURE PRIVATISATION OF THE BRITISH COAL CORPORATION

1.97 In announcing its intention to privatise the British Coal Corporation (BCC) the Government stated its commitment to ensuring that standards of health and safety are maintained after privatisation.

1.98 HSC set out its position on this in response to a request for advice from the Minister of State for Trade and Industry. HSC considered that the future health and safety regime should be founded upon two principles:

- a comprehensive health and safety regulatory regime under which standards of health and safety in the industry will be maintained and improved, should be in place in time. To this end HSC have published two consultative documents setting out proposals which will give legal status to certain of BCC's existing owners' instructions relating to the prevention of inrushes, ventilation, fire and frictional ignitions; and

- the Commission should continue to be the health and safety regulatory body for the industry, and HSE the enforcement authority.

1.99 When it is known what form privatisation will take the arrangements covering rescue, research and other areas of safety where BCC currently undertakes a central role for the industry may also need to be reviewed.

THE GOVERNMENT'S RENEWED DEREGULATION INITIATIVE

1.100 In early 1993 the Government's deregulation initiative was given renewed impetus, with a commitment by Ministers that all existing legislation should be reviewed and unnecessary burdens on industry removed. In January 1993 HSC accepted Ministers' invitation to undertake such a *review of existing health and safety legislation*. HSC has a continuing role to ensure that necessary standards of health and safety are maintained or improved. The aim of the review is to examine whether there are obligations arising for business which can be eased or simplified without endangering such standards. To this end the review, on which HSC will be advised by seven industrial Task Groups, will be testing each piece of legislation against the following criteria:

• is the law still relevant and needed? If so,

• what are the compliance and enforcement costs which the law places on business?

• do the potential benefits still justify the legislation?

The review will pay specific attention to the impact of health and safety legislation on small firms and the self-employed.

1.101 HSE established a dedicated review team in January 1993 and Employment Ministers approved the detailed workplan for the review submitted in March. There will be extensive consultations with business during the review, and business, trade union and local authority interests are represented on the Steering Group overseeing its work. The review is expected substantially to be completed by April 1994.

1.102 HSC also seconded an official to work on a scrutiny led by Department of Trade and Industry on the *implementation and enforcement of EC directives*. The scrutiny looked at many case studies, including the EC Health and Safety Framework Directive and five associated directives as a case study.

Chapter 2 CROSS-SECTORAL HEALTH AND SAFETY HAZARDS

2.1   This chapter sets out the main activities of the Health and Safety Commission and HSE on hazards which apply across different sectors of industry. They range from detailed work on assessing the risk from specific chemicals to improving awareness of the musculoskeletal risks involved in handling loads. They are not in any particular order of priority.

HAZARDOUS SUBSTANCES

Notification, classification and risk assessment

2.2   The *successful control of chemicals* - in the home, workplace or the environment - depends on knowing how dangerous they are. Armed with this information, the user can begin to make an objective assessment of the dangers and introduce appropriate controls. In the past year significant progress has been made in enhancing the information provided by suppliers to users.

*   In the UK a consultative document on the proposed *Chemicals (Hazard Information and Packaging) Regulations (CHIP)* was issued. The regulations will require chemicals to be considered for environmental, human and physico-chemical effects before they are sold. If dangerous, the chemicals will require safety data sheets and informative labels. Following consultation revised regulations were submitted to the Secretary of State.

*   In the EC agreement was reached on a number of *technical amendments* to the directives on which CHIP is based. These changes clarify some difficult areas such as the consideration of chemicals for effects on reproduction and the labelling of gas cylinders.

*   The United Nations Conference on Environment and Development held in Rio de Janeiro in 1992 agreed to develop a *global classification scheme for chemicals* by the year 2000 (see paragraph 1.30).

2.3   These developments present major changes which will improve health and safety standards and assist those who market chemicals internationally. However smaller, non-exporting firms may find it difficult to understand some of the more complex issues and HSE has therefore made special efforts to develop advice, with the help of industry, *aimed specifically at small and non-expert firms.*

Notification of new substances

2.4   To help ensure that the potential of new chemical substances to cause harm to people or the environment is assessed before they are placed on the European Community market, manufacturers and importers are required to provide the relevant competent authority with information about a substance's properties, uses and quantities. The efficient, rapid and cost-effective processing of applications to ensure completion within the required deadlines has continued to be a priority for HSE. During the year around 90 UK notifications, about 100 Limited Announcements and some 250 summaries of notifications from other member states were processed.

2.5   A procedure for exchanging summary information on newly notified substances, on disk, in all member states was introduced in February 1993 with the goal of reducing, and eventually virtually eliminating, the circulation and storage of traditional paper-based documentation. HSE was awarded, and during the year largely completed work on, two major contracts in the area of information exchange, and in addition has contributed extensively to work on special procedures at EC level to define the borderline between polymers and notifiable substances.

2.6   In June 1992 the European Commission published the **_7th Amendment to the Dangerous Substances Directive_** which brought in new requirements for notification. Among these are provisions for:

- harmonising the data requirements for the notification of substances in low quantities across the whole of the EC;

- reducing the amount of testing on animals; and

- reducing the amount of information required when a substance is being used for research and development.

2.7   Most importantly, the directive introduces the requirement for competent authorities to carry out **_risk assessments on notified substances_** and, if necessary, to make recommendations for risk reduction measures. These new requirements will be implemented by the Notification of New Substances Regulations 1993. It is proposed that the UK competent authority will be HSE and DoE acting jointly.

2.8   HSC published a consultative document in January 1993. Regulations implementing this part of the directive are expected to be made before the end of 1993.

Notification of existing substances

2.9   The EC **_regulation on the evaluation and control of existing substances_** (defined as those on the market between January 1971 and September 1981) was adopted in March 1993 and came directly into force in member states two months later. The regulation requires manufacturers and importers to submit to the European Commission data on substances produced or imported in high tonnages. The data will be used to draw up priority lists of substances. Competent authorities in member states will carry out risk assessments on these substances. As with new substances, it is envisaged that HSE and DoE will together undertake the duties of competent authority in the UK.

Risk assessment of new and existing substances

2.10 HSE has been active in EC negotiations to establish the principles to be embodied in the forthcoming directive on the **_risk assessment of new substances._** This was adopted in April 1993, and will provide the legislative basis for the risk assessment of new substances notified under the requirements of the 7th Amendment to the Dangerous Substances Directive (see 2.6 above). A member of HSE staff on secondment to the EC has helped draft the directive; and HSE bid successfully for a contract with the European Commission to produce the technical guidance notes which will accompany it. Negotiations on a corresponding Commission directive to support the forthcoming Existing Substances Regulation will begin in autumn 1993.

2.11 All of these initiatives emphasise the shift internationally over the past few years towards **_seeking to control hazards at the point of supply._** This makes the distinction between consumer safety, environmental protection and worker health and safety less clear-cut. HSE has therefore been in close co-operation with other Government Departments in taking this work forward.

Control of hazardous substances in the workplace

2.12 Controls on the supply of chemicals described above have to be complemented by controls on their use. The Control of Substances Hazardous to Health Regulations 1988 (COSHH), provides the legislative framework for this control in the UK, supplemented by regulations on specific substances such as lead and asbestos. Main developments in 1992/93 included:

- *Improved COSHH guidance:* A new, free guide for employers on the requirements of COSHH was prepared to replace three existing HSE leaflets on the regulations. *COSHH: a brief guide for employers* sets out the successive stages involved in complying with the regulations, and pays particular attention to the assessment process.

- *COSHH enforcement:* Inspectors have continued to enforce the provisions of the COSHH Regulations, where appropriate using multi-disciplinary teams during inspection and investigations. Enforcement initiatives included biological monitoring of workers exposed to cadmium; a publicity drive to make farmers engaged in sheep-dipping better aware of the application of COSHH to the hazards involved; and participation in a seminar on the hazardous substances used in dental surgeries.

- *Exposure limits:* HSC agreed to consultation on ten proposals for new or revised maximum exposure limits (MELs) for inhalation of particular substances and a proposal to increase the reference period for short term limits from 10 to 15 minutes. HSC also adopted nine new or revised limits to the list of occupational exposure standards (OESs) and agreed to consultation on a further seven proposals. It also withdrew the OES for o-toluidine pending the assignment of a MEL. HSC has also published the data used in setting OESs.

Carcinogens at work

2.13 COSHH was used to implement the main requirements of the EC *Carcinogens Directive* from 1 January 1993. A seminar on occupational cancer, 'Cancer in the workplace: reducing risks and promoting health', was held during European Cancer Week in October 1992 to publicise the implementation of the directive.

2.14 Two new sets of regulations on *asbestos* came into force on 1 January 1993: the Control of Asbestos at Work (Amendment) Regulations 1992, and the Asbestos (Prohibition) Regulations 1992. These implemented two EC asbestos directives adopted in 1991 which amend the 1983 Asbestos Worker Protection Directive and the 1976 Marketing and Use Directive. The new regulations also implement the Carcinogens Directive insofar as it applies to asbestos. Two revised asbestos ACoPs were also published, one giving practical guidance on the Control of Asbestos at Work Regulations while the other, more specialised ACoP covered work with asbestos insulation, coating and insulating board. The latter strongly encourages the adoption of wet-strip methods to remove asbestos insulation and coating as a practical way of reducing the amount of asbestos dust that can be produced by using dry-strip methods. Both revised ACoPs place a firmer emphasis on using accredited laboratories for measuring asbestos in air levels, particularly those accredited for asbestos sampling and analysis by the National Measurement and Accreditation Service (NAMAS).

Chemical Agents Directive

2.15 HSE officials were involved in preliminary discussions of the proposed EC Chemical Agents Directive, which among other things will consolidate controls of hazardous chemicals in the workplace, but the negotiations foreshadowed in the Plan are not due to begin until later in the year.

PESTICIDES

2.16 HSE is responsible for the registration of non-agricultural pesticides. The efficient, rapid and cost effective processing of applications for approval remains a priority and approvals continue to be processed without delay. Over 900 approval applications and amendments were processed in 1992/93, and some 9000 enquiries were answered.

2.17 Liaison between HSE and the non-agricultural pesticides industry has been broadened by means of a working group to respond to an EC proposal for a directive on *biocides*. The working group comprises about 40 members drawn from all sectors of the biocides industry, together with representatives of trade unions and environmental organisations.

2.18 The use of pesticides continues to give rise to public concern and HSE assigns a high priority to investigation of incidents involving these chemicals. In 1992/93, all reported incidents and complaints in non-agricultural situations were investigated. One reason for this was to test the level of awareness and impact of recent publications concerning training and safe use of pesticides. For example, the solvent used in timber treatment in domestic dwellings may present risks to occupiers and neighbours as well as to the operatives, if the guidance is not carefully followed.

Pesticides left unattended in a public place for several days

2.19 Developments during 1992/93 included:

- the production of 36 guidance notes to assist local authorities in their enforcement of the Control of Pesticides Regulations 1986 (COPR);

- in conjunction with the British Wood Preserving and Damp-proofing Association, a study of exposure to wood treatment chemicals arising from in situ remedial treatment of timber;

- in conjunction with the Department of the Environment, implementation of the 9th Amendment to the Marketing and Use Directive concerning pentachlorophenol; and

- completion of the lindane and tributyl tin oxide reviews and the initiation of special reviews on copper compounds and pentachlorophenol.

Veterinary medicines

2.20 Many veterinary medicines are substances hazardous to health and their use at work is subject to COSHH. HSE commissioned or undertook during 1992/93:

Photograph of areas of
skin contaminated with
dilute sheep dip

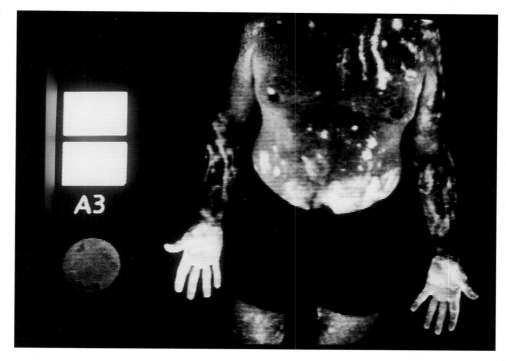

- publication of a booklet, *Veterinary medicines: safe use by farmers and other animal handlers,* giving guidance on compliance with COSHH to those who work with veterinary medicines;

- a project to establish the quantities of veterinary medicines stored, the conditions of storage and the level of competence of users such as farmers and their employees;

- an occupational hygiene assessment of sheep dipping practices and processes; and

- an investigation into the possible chronic neuropsychological and neurological effects on sheep farmers of occupational exposure to organophosphorus compounds.

2.21 During the year, HSE scientists developed a way of making visible, parts of the human body contaminated by liquids such as **sheep dip**. A fluorescent tracer is added to the dip solution. A special lighting arrangement causes the contaminated skin to glow in the dark, and the results are photographed. A way of measuring how much of the insecticide enters the body, by measuring breakdown products in the urine, has also been devised. Taken together, such studies provide useful information to help identify routes of exposure, so that effective control measures can be developed.

**TRANSPORT OF
DANGEROUS
GOODS**

2.22 The revisions of the ***Road Tanker and Packaged Goods Regulations*** came into force in June 1992, together with a new revision of the Road Tanker Approved List. The Road Traffic (Training of Drivers of Vehicles Carrying Dangerous Goods) Regulations 1992 came into force in July 1992. HSC approved four ACoPs on the design and construction of certain types of road tanker to come into force on 1 June 1993. Publication was delayed by the need to agree the text with the European Commission, which was done in early 1993. Work has started on harmonising current regulations for the carriage of dangerous goods with the relevant international agreements. It is planned to publish consultative documents during 1993.

2.23 HSE inspectors investigated a number of *incidents involving the transport of dangerous substances.* These included:

- one in which a petrol tanker overturned, following a collision with another vehicle, leading to an escape of petrol through splits in the tanker shell. The petrol was quickly ignited, 42 cars were burnt out in the fire and many houses and a nearby swimming-bath had to be evacuated;

- another in which an unmarked container of sulphuric acid burst on a trailer as a police officer was about to stop the driver of the tractor. Acid spilt on to both the road and the police car and the fire brigade had to be called to wash it away. The tractor owner was later prosecuted by HSE.

2.24 In order to encourage operators to comply with the regulations relating to the transport of dangerous substances, HSE inspectors took part in several *roadside checks on vehicles.* These included a large-scale exercise based on the crossings over the river Thames in East London. Other roadside checks were carried out with the police or the Vehicle Inspectorate, as well as joint police/HSE mobile checks. During the year 985 vehicles were examined, 286 were found to be contravening the regulations and 68 were prohibited from continuing their journey until defects had been remedied.

2.25 Following one of the recommendations made in the ACDS report on the *major hazard aspects of the transport of dangerous substances,* a detailed study was undertaken to assess the risks from the handling of such substances in three ports/terminals. A simple risk analysis indicated that the risks of such operations might be unacceptable. However, the study showed that risks to the individual and to society were broadly acceptable, though measures could be taken to reduce these risks still further. The recommendations made in the follow-up study are being actively pursued.

FIRE AND EXPLOSION

Explosives

2.26 To promote compliance with the relevant legislation, the Explosives Inspectorate increased its inspection activity by some 20% in 1992/93 as compared to 1991/92.

2.27 During the year, negotiations on the EC directive on the *supervision and placing on the market of explosives for civil uses* moved ahead rapidly. This directive has a very short time-scale for implementation and urgent work has begun on a new set of regulations to implement both the security and safety aspects by September 1993.

2.28 The directive has required work to begin on collating and reviewing all UK *national standards for explosives* to produce a manual of standards and test methods in collaboration with industry. These will form the UK requirements during the transitional period under the directive and the UK position in negotiation of CEN harmonised standards.

Still from video of petrol tanker fire

Shotfiring at a quarry

2.29 Work has continued, in consultation with representatives of the explosives industry and others affected, on new or revised regulations covering:

- the manufacture and storage of explosives;

- the carriage of explosives by road;

- the classification and labelling of explosives; and

- marking of plastic explosives for detection.

The consultative documents foreshadowed in the Plan are now likely to be issued over the next eighteen months.

2.30 New technology in the explosives industry has been developed to supply blasting explosives for shotfiring at quarries using *mixer trucks for on-site manufacture of explosives.* Mixer trucks carrying non-explosive oxidisers move from quarry to quarry and provide a fill for shot-holes which only develops explosive characteristics when in the shot-hole itself. There are substantial safety advantages in this approach. The Explosives Inspectorate and the industry co-operated fully in developing the legal basis for such operations.

2.31 Other significant developments include:

- establishment of an *Enforcement Liaison Committee for Transport of Explosives* (ELCTEX). Membership brings together HSE and other Government Departments and agencies concerned with the transport of explosives. It will review the full range of operational controls, procedures and guidance.

- The HSE/CBI (Explosives Industry Group) Working Group on Explosives has produced guidance in two important areas - the fire resistance of explosives vehicles and the carriage of mixed loads. These guidance documents have been published by the CBI and address recommendations for further work made in the HSE report into the Peterborough explosion and the ACDS report on major hazard aspects of the transport of dangerous substances.

Flammable solids, liquids and gases

2.32 Following the extension in March 1992 of the Commission's responsibilities on gas safety, consultation has begun on proposals for regulations and ACoP to replace the gas safety elements in the Gas Quality Regulations 1972 and 1983, which are needed to meet the changing nature of the gas supply market.

2.33 The *Council for Registered Gas Installers* (CORGI) is now well established, and lending increasing, valuable support to HSE's enforcement efforts to raise standards of gas fitting work. HSE continues to work with the industry and other bodies including the Gas Consumers Council to increase public awareness of gas safety. In the light of several tragic deaths, specific publicity initiatives have focused on students, and the need for landlords to maintain gas appliances.

2.34 Other developments include:

- work has continued on the revision of the Gas Safety (Installation and Use) Regulations 1984, and its accompanying ACoP. A consultative document should be published during 1993;

- the proposals for revised regulatory *controls for petrol containers* better to meet market needs have been delayed by the need to consult the European Commission. HSE hopes to begin formal consultation in the latter half of 1993 with new regulations in operation in early 1994;

- the HSE guidance booklet HS(G)41 on the *construction and operation of petrol filling stations* has been reviewed and updated to take account of technological developments in several areas. Consultation will take place during the summer of 1993 with publication of the revised guidance planned for early 1994.

2.35 While highly flammable substances are generally treated with caution, this is not always so with higher flash point liquids or solids, and there have been some serious incidents during the handling and storage of ostensibly low-risk materials, as the following fatal accidents illustrate.

- Two men lost their lives on board a berthed oil bulk ore carrier vessel which had discharged its cargo of coal, when vapours from a previous liquid cargo were ignited after ballasting operations.

Domestic gas explosion

- One life was lost, and others could have been, when vapours from a high flash point oil ignited after faults with the steam heating system of a storage vessel led to the oil being heated well above its flash point. The resultant fire caused a nearby tank to be projected 40 metres into the air.

2.36 Guidance has been drafted on the *safe use of flammable liquids* and *use of bitumen in quarries,* which should increase awareness of the potential dangers, and help prevent further incidents in the future.

Fire precautions

2.37 Responsibility for the enforcement of risks from fires at places of work is shared between HSE and fire authorities. New guidance on *the basic principles of liaison between HSE and fire authorities*, under the existing legislative regime, has been agreed between the Home Departments and HSE. This has been issued as a joint circular.

2.38 The Appleton Report (referred to in Chapter 1) on stoppages caused by fire and bomb threats on mass transit systems, eg London Underground, drew attention to value of risk assessment in determining safety priorities. *Assessment of risk* is central to the *Framework and its associated directives*. HSE is making its expertise on risk assessment available to the Home Office as they develop revised proposals to implement the fire elements of the directives.

2.39 There have been several serious fires involving stores of paper, plastic and rubber tyres. Work is well advanced on new guidance to deal with the storage of these materials.

MAJOR CHEMICAL HAZARDS

2.40 The proposal for a new EC directive on the ***control of major accident hazards*** following the review of the Seveso directive did not progress as rapidly as expected and is due to be published in autumn 1993.

2.41 HSE has received over 660 ***CIMAH safety reports.*** Following an initial evaluation, these are subject to a longer term, multi-disciplinary assessment and are used as key documents for reference during preventive inspection.

2.42 The potential hazards presented by major chemical plant were brought home by a number of major incidents during the year including the following:

- during cleaning of residue from a distillation vessel used to recover an aromatic nitro compound, an incandescent flame erupted from the vessel scorching a path through a nearby building before hitting a large office block. Two employees were killed instantly and three others, including a young office worker, died from their injuries several days after the incident. The company, Hickson and Welch Ltd, was prosecuted for an alleged breach of Section 2(1) of the HSWA and fined £250 000. Costs totalling £150 000 were awarded to HSE;

Trail of damage caused by flame from a distillation vessel at Hickson and Welch Ltd

- a runaway exothermic reaction in a reactor vessel in a chemical factory resulted in the release of 3.5 tonnes of chemicals, blown by the wind 4 kilometres from the site. Thirty people were admitted to hospital for observation. The company, Namepak Ltd (formerly International Biosynthetics) was prosecuted for offences under Sections 2 and 3 of the HSWA and fined £4000.

2.43 HSE hosted an international conference on the major hazard aspects of *land use planning* in October 1992 as part of the programme during the UK Presidency. HSE continued to work closely with the Department of the Environment (DoE) and the Scottish Office on the introduction of their planning controls for hazardous substances. The Planning (Hazardous Substances) Regulations 1992 came into force in England and Wales on 1 June 1992 and equivalent legislation in Scotland on 1 May 1993.

2.44 These controls placed HSE's long standing role in land use planning on a statutory footing. In 1992/93 HSE advised local authorities on 4823 applications for development in the vicinity of major hazards. Most were dealt with by inspectors based in HSE area offices, but some 795 were referred to the Major Hazards Assessment Unit for more specialised scrutiny.

2.45 In the great majority of cases local planning authorities follow HSE's advice. In one case, however, a local authority in the North of England was minded to grant planning permission against HSE's advice in circumstances which were felt to be of serious concern. For only the second time in 20 years, HSE took the exceptional step of referring the case to the Secretary of State for the Environment. A local public inquiry was held in February 1993, following which the Secretary of State for the Environment accepted HSE's advice that planning permission should be refused on grounds of safety.

MACHINERY SAFETY

Machinery

2.46 Regulations to implement the EC Article 118A Directive on the provision and use of work equipment (including machinery) were introduced with effect from 1 January 1993 and will come fully into force on 1 January 1997. That directive is connected to the EC Article 100A Directive on the supply of new machinery, which has been implemented by DTI regulations. These also came into effect on 1 January 1993 but will not become mandatory until 1 January 1995; they will then begin to be enforced by HSE inspectors in respect of new machinery supplied for use at work. Meanwhile initial integrity of machinery is being emphasised in discussions with both manufacturers and suppliers; inspectors have been trained on this issue.

2.47 A large number of accidents are still caused by *failure to provide elementary protective devices.* For example, a young inexperienced operator was attempting to remove a jammed component from between the tools of an inadequately guarded power press, when the press operated, amputating three fingers. The firm was subsequently prosecuted.

2.48 Exchanges of information between firms in the same industry can prevent further accidents. In one case, an employee was shot through the thigh when a thin sliver of metal was ejected from a rolling mill. The company was put in touch with another firm identified by the Molten Metals National Interest Group as having experienced similar incidents of metal ejecting and developed a front guard and interlocked rear enclosure to cure the problem.

Lift trucks

2.49 An extensive revision of HSE's guidance booklet *Safety in working with lift trucks* was completed. The guidance now takes into account the recently introduced regulations on workplace health and safety, and on the use of work equipment. It emphasises the need for employers to assess their lift truck operations and introduce safe systems of work to eliminate or reduce the risks from lift trucks.

ELECTICITY 2.50 Electricity continues to be a cause of fatal accidents in many employment sectors. Contact with underground cables in particular involves workers in the construction industry. Contact with *overhead power lines* involves employees from a wide range of industries, for example:

- two men were killed while using a lorry-mounted crane to remove a scrap car from a customer's premises; the crane touched 11 000 volt overhead power lines; and

- a labourer assisting with a groundwork survey on farm land died after his 5-metre metal measuring staff contacted 11 000 volt overhead lines.

2.51 In response to numerous such incidents in agriculture, HSE produced a video warning of the dangers of power lines on farms. An information sheet for farmers is also proposed. This information will complement existing publications such as our guidance note *Avoidance of danger from overhead lines*, which stresses the simple precautions needed to prevent these accidents.

2.52 Inspectors receive many requests for information and advice concerning the legal requirement to *maintain electrical equipment*, both fixed and portable. A new HSE guidance note on maintenance of portable electrical equipment is being prepared. In the interim an HSE information sheet on this subject was issued in early 1993. This and related initiatives have sought to dispel the tendencies of some consultants and others promoting their services to oversell the requirement of the legislation.

PROGRAMMABLE ELECTRONIC SYSTEMS 2.53 *Remote diagnosis of machinery faults* has been developing quickly over the last few years. It offers benefits to the user, but also raises a number of potential safety problems. To facilitate the development of these systems while maintaining adequate levels of safety, HSE, in collaboration with industry, has developed guidelines on the safety aspects that need to be considered. During 1992/93 public consultation took place on a draft HSE guidance document, which it is planned to publish in early 1994.

2.54 Most machine tools now use computer numerical control (CNC) and many have a central programmable device which supervises the operation of slave programmable controllers, each responsible for the operation of a single actuator. This complexity, coupled with a requirement for close access to powered dangerous parts, have made conventional interlocking impractical. During the year HSE and the Machine Tool Trades Association collaborated to produce a guidance document on standards of interlocking guards.

2.55 During 1992 there was important progress on three key standards, in the development of which HSE have been closely involved:

- a draft European standard on safe control systems for machines reached the public comment stage;

- a draft International Standard on the functional safety of electric/electronic/programmable systems was issued as a consultative document; and

- a draft International Standard on safety-related software has been put out for public comment.

2.56 *Control systems* play an increasing role in the functioning of machinery and plant in all sectors. In order to draw attention to the possible safety problems if inadequate attention is paid to their design and maintenance, HSE is working on a publication called *Out of control*. Consultation has already taken place and publication is expected in 1993.

Reconstruction showing the effect of a crane coming into contact with an overhead power line

MANUAL HANDLING OF LOADS

2.57 Following a very helpful public consultation exercise, the Health and Safety Commission approved proposals for regulations and guidance to implement the EC directive on manual handling. The Manual Handling Operations Regulations came into force on 1 January 1993 along with regulations implementing the Framework and associated directives (see paragraphs 1.17-1.23). HSC hope that the regulations will help to reduce the very great number of injuries associated with manual handling - over one quarter of those reported to HSE each year.

2.58 The regulations set out a hierarchy of steps that employers should take to reduce the risk of manual handling injuries:

- avoid the need for hazardous manual handling, so far as is reasonably practicable;

- where such operations cannot be avoided, assess them; and

- based on the assessment, take steps to reduce the risk of injury to the lowest level reasonably practicable.

2.59 HSE's general guidance explains the requirements, how assessments should be carried out, and offers suggestions on how employers may reduce the risk of injury. HSC is encouraging the production of industry-specific guidance on manual handling and its Health Services Advisory Committee has published *Guidance on the manual handling of loads in the health services*. Other Industry Advisory Committees are considering the need for guidance in their areas of responsibility.

WORK RELATED UPPER LIMB DISORDERS

2.60 A major HSE campaign, 'Lighten the load', was launched in September 1991 to raise awareness of musculoskeletal disorders (ie problems affecting muscles, joints, tendons or back). The first phase targeted upper limb disorders. Over 750 000 campaign leaflets were given out during the first year. A survey asked employers who had received leaflets or other campaign material to rate them for presentation and relevance - over 73% rated it as good or very good.

2.61 HSE has encouraged a number of successful measures by employers, for example:

- in the poultry industry, one firm reduced the number of days lost from wrist problems from 125 to 24 over three years by preventive measures including pre-employment interviews, job rotation, education of operators and managers and improved ergonomic design of workstations;

- in the food industry, a company developed a device which removed the need for some manual operations that were thought to cause painful upper limb disorders;

- an engineering firm had a high incidence of sickness absence and civil claims resulting from poor job design, operation and organisation. Inexpensive solutions such as adjustments to the height of working surfaces, improved seating and re-organised working methods reduced the risks from excessive lifting, bending, twisting and reaching.

DISPLAY SCREEN EQUIPMENT

2.62 Consultation on the proposed *regulations and guidance on work with display screen equipment* attracted a widespread interest and comments from over 300 organisations. Room for manoeuvre was limited by the need to implement the EC directive, but in response to a call for protection of freelance workers known to be at risk, HSC extended some employer duties to cover the self-employed working at employers' workstations. The regulations came into force on 1 January 1993. HSE's promotional strategy, described in Chapter 1, ensured continuing high levels of interest and enquiries. By March approximately 425 000 copies of the employee guidance and 98 000 booklets for employers had been issued.

2.63 In July 1992 the results of an important research project commissioned by HSE on work with VDUs were published. This, the first study in the UK of the effects of VDU work on pregnant women, found no evidence of any increased risk of miscarriage. This confirmed most previous international studies, and HSE advice, that pregnant women need not stop VDU work.

NOISE AND VIBRATION

2.64 The action undertaken by inspectors to enforce *the Noise at Work Regulations 1989* was maintained at the levels achieved in the two previous years. In addition, 14 companies

Mobile exhibition on noise at work

were prosecuted under the regulations, principally for failure to comply with the requirements to conduct a noise assessment.

2.65 HSE also stepped up its publicity efforts to raise awareness and change attitudes to noise in industry. It built on earlier advertising in Scotland and the West Midlands and extended its radio campaign into the Greater Manchester area. As part of HSE's contribution to the European Year of Safety, Hygiene and Health Protection at Work, a mobile exhibition on noise at work toured the country. HSE also sponsored a special category on noise under the Young Engineer for Britain competition.

2.66 Work continued on an *evaluation of the Noise at Work Regulations* following an exercise conducted by HSE inspectors during 1991/92 to assess the level of understanding of and compliance with the regulations by employers. Results will be published in spring 1994.

Physical Agents Directive

2.67 HSE made preliminary contributions on proposals by the European Commission for a directive to protect workers from risks associated with a range of *physical agents*: initially noise; hand-arm vibration; whole body vibration; and non-ionising electro-magnetic radiation, but other agents could be added later. The EC published its draft directive at the end of the year: and HSC considered the principal issues for negotiations due to begin in 1993.

RADIATION Ionising radiations

2.68 The proposals for revision of the *basic safety standards for radiation protection* did not in the event reach the European Council during the year. In the meantime, HSE began consideration of the consequent revision of the Ionising Radiations Regulations 1985 (IRR 85). The Public Information for Radiation Emergencies Regulations 1992 were made on 26 November 1992, implementing a Euratom directive.

2.69 Guidance for employers' and employees' representatives on the assessment and management of work in order to restrict exposure to ionising radiation was published in December 1992. This publication complements the practical guidance given in the fourth part of the ACoP supporting IRR 85, which was published in 1991.

2.70 HSC approved draft regulations, supported by an ACoP, to implement a Euratom directive on 'outside workers' (generally itinerant or contract workers working away from their employers' sites). Formal notification to the European Commission as required by the Euratom Treaty took place in March 1993 as scheduled, with a view to the regulations being submitted to Ministers later in the year and coming into force on 1 January 1994.

2.71 In a few member states, certain aspects of radiation protection depended on customs checks at national borders which stopped from 1 January 1993, under the Single Market. The European Commission therefore proposed a previously unheralded Council Regulation introducing new requirements for all *cross-border shipments of radioactive substances*. In negotiations on this, HSC/E's objective has been to secure an agreement which satisfies those member states who need this requirement without placing undue burdens on UK industry.

Childhood cancer and radiation

2.72 Work continued on studies to examine the reported associations between childhood leukaemia and paternal employment in the nuclear industry. HSE's epidemiological case-control study based on the children of workers who had been employed at the Sellafield reprocessing site was extended to cover all childhood cancers. A report on this study was published in October 1993. A short guide to the six separate studies commissioned jointly by HSE and the Department of Health was published in December 1992. Some of these projects will not be completed until 1995/96.

Non-ionising electromagnetic radiation

2.73 A research project by the National Radiological Protection Board and funded by HSE was undertaken to identify the areas of industry that are likely to be affected by the proposed requirements on NIEMR in the Physical Agents Directive. Research work was also commissioned in areas of measurement of non-ionising electromagnetic radiation, partly in support of information required for handling the proposed directive (see paragraph 2.67 above).

BIOTECHNOLOGY AND GENETIC MODIFICATION

2.74 Regulations implementing EC directives on the contained use and deliberate release of *genetically modified organisms* (GMOs) came into force on 1 February 1993. They replace and build on the Genetic Manipulation Regulations 1989, and are designed to protect both human health and the environment.

2.75 After extensive consultation by HSE and the Department of the Environment (DoE), the regulations were structured to follow the format of the two directives as closely as possible. The Genetically Modified Organisms (Contained Use) Regulations 1992, for which HSE has responsibility, were made under the Health and Safety at Work Act, while the Genetically Modified Organisms (Deliberate Release) Regulations 1992 were introduced by DoE under part VI of the Environmental Protection Act 1990. The combined legal effect of the directives and UK parent law meant that an additional set of regulations, the Genetically Modified Organisms (Contained Use) Regulations 1993, made under the Environmental Protection Act, was required to cover environmental risks associated with contained use of genetically modified larger plants and animals.

2.76 The regulations are jointly administered by HSE and DoE, in collaboration with the Ministry of Agriculture, Fisheries and Food, the Scottish Office and the Welsh Office. Inspection and enforcement for both sets of regulations are carried out by HSE specialist inspectors. In the case of the Deliberate Release Regulations this is done under an agency agreement with DoE.

2.77 Together with the University of Salford, HSE set up two conferences at the beginning of 1993 aimed at explaining the new regulatory system to notifiers. Both conferences were well attended.

2.78 Under the chairmanship of Professor Sir Hans Kornberg FRS, the Advisory Committee on Genetic Modification (ACGM) will advise HSC/E on the human health and safety aspects of the contained use of GMOs. It will also advise Ministers with environmental responsibilities in other Government Departments on the environmental aspects of such work. All ACGM guidance notes will be updated to take account of the new regulatory system.

2.79 The year has seen important changes for the Advisory Committee on Releases to the Environment (ACRE), which is chaired by Professor John Beringer CBE. ACRE was set up in 1990 as an HSC Committee operated jointly with DoE. From 1 February 1993 it became a statutory committee under section 124 of the Environmental Protection Act 1990, appointed by the Secretary of State for the Environment to advise on GMO releases. Although the committee will continue to deal primarily with environmental concerns, it will also advise HSC/E on any human health and safety aspects of releases.

2.80 There was an increase in the number of inspection visits conducted under the Genetic Manipulation Regulations 1989 during the year. This led to a total of six enforcement notices (two Prohibition, four Improvement) being issued.

BIOLOGICAL AGENTS AND PATHOGENS

2.81 Proposals for implementing an EC directive on the protection of workers from risks related to *exposure to biological agents* were published in a consultative document issued on 8 April 1993. The proposals include a number of minor amendments and the addition of a new schedule to the COSHH Regulations, together with a new supplementary Approved Code of Practice. The Health and Safety (Dangerous Pathogens) Regulations 1981 will be replaced by new notification requirements under COSHH.

2.82 The Biological Agents Directive also contains provisions for the adoption of a *Community classification of biological agents*. A proposal for a supplementary directive was published in August 1992, and negotiations reached a conclusion at a meeting of the EC Council of Social Affairs Ministers in early April 1993. In anticipation of this outcome, HSE did much preliminary work on a revision of the *Categorisation of pathogens according to hazard and categories of containment* drawn up by the Advisory Committee on Dangerous Pathogens (ACDP), which will form an 'Approved List' under COSHH when the Classification Directive is implemented.

2.83 As well as providing expert advice in relation to the two directives on biological agents, ACDP continued its work on a number of other matters. A fourth edition of the ACDP guidance on HIV, which will be expanded to include other blood-borne infections, is now being prepared (see paragraph 2.90 below), while new guidance on work with transmissible spongiform encephalopathies is almost complete.

Zoonoses

2.84 A guidance booklet, *The occupational zoonoses*, originally produced for HSE inspectors and the Employment Medical Advisory Service, was published early in 1993. The booklet provides information on seventeen zoonotic infections, including details of their sources and appropriate preventive measures.

2.85 Three research projects concerned with zoonotic infections are continuing. Two involve examination of the incidence of zoonoses among agricultural workers, while the third is related to the transmission of Lyme disease.

Legionnaires' disease

2.86 New regulations requiring *the notification to local authorities of all premises containing wet cooling towers* or evaporative condensers came into force on 2 November 1992. Notifications will provide investigators with valuable information on the location of such installations in the event of an outbreak of disease.

2.87 During 1992/93 HSE inspectors carried out a series of special visits as part of an evaluation of the effectiveness of the ACoP, *The prevention or control of legionellosis, including legionnaires' disease*, which came into force in January 1992. The evaluation process will continue into the coming year.

2.88 Work began on a revision of the guidance booklet HS(G)70, *The control of legionellosis including legionnaires' disease*, in consultation with experts in the field.

2.89 Further progress was made with commissioned work on a model cooling tower held in containment and deliberately infected with bacteria including legionella. The aim of the project is to investigate the dynamics of colonisation by legionella and other organisms and to develop strategies for decontamination and limitation of growth in cooling systems.

AIDS

2.90 Although the number of cases of HIV in the population continues to rise steadily, the risk of occupational infection is acknowledged to be low. Nonetheless the need to keep employees informed and alert has led to the preparation of a more comprehensive edition of the ACDP guidance on HIV *(HIV -the causative agent of AIDS and related conditions)*.

2.91 As part of the campaign to promote employee awareness, leaflets and guidance were issued which stressed among other matters the negligible risk to fellow workers or the public from normal occupational or social contact with HIV. Specific guidance was also made available to people involved in health care work, emergency service workers, cleaners or custodial workers, who may be at risk from accidental exposure to body fluids or discarded needles. Advice on the general hygiene precautions to be taken when administering first aid in the workplace was also published.

PASSIVE SMOKING AT WORK

2.92 The health effects of passive smoking - both generally and in the workplace - have become a particular focus for public concern. In October HSE published a revised version of its booklet *Passive smoking at work*. The booklet encourages employers to develop policies on smoking in the workplace in consultation with the workforce and sets out ways by which a smoke-free environment for non-smokers can be achieved.

SICK BUILDING SYNDROME

2.93 In August HSE published a review commissioned from the Building Research Establishment of the evidence on causes of and solutions for sick building syndrome (SBS). Despite the existence of extensive research, the review concluded that the causes of SBS could not be clearly established and the problem was unlikely to be eradicated in the short term. The review identified a number of risk factors associated with SBS but emphasised the limited evidence for any being a direct causal agent. However the review does suggest that the application of current knowledge can achieve improvements. HSE is currently working on guidance which reflects this.

MENTAL HEALTH

2.94 Mental health problems - including stress, anxiety and depression - are now recognised as a major cause of ill health and sickness absence at work. HSE has funded a selective literature review to identify the commonly agreed causal factors of occupational stress and strategies for dealing with them. In the light of the findings HSE will consider the need for basic guidance for employers. More generally, HSE has continued to encourage employers to recognise the benefits of policies to promote mental health in the workplace.

DRUG ABUSE

2.95 In November HSE published a revised and updated version of its free leaflet *Drug abuse at work - a guide to employers* which aims to help employers establish a policy to minimise drug abuse and encourage employees with drug problems to come forward for treatment.

VIOLENCE TO STAFF

2.96 HSE continued to raise awareness of the problem of violence to staff by promoting a structured approach to managing and reducing it. Initiatives during 1992/93 included:

- a seminar focusing on violence to public transport employees;

- the production of a consultation document on draft guidance on preventing violence to staff in the financial sector;

- collating the results of a nationwide survey by HSE inspectors and local authorities to evaluate the effectiveness of HSE's current guidance on preventing violence, and to assess the need for any further work.

2.97 Although this is a relatively new area for employers and HSE alike, enforcement action has already been taken against a local authority to implement systems of work to reduce the risk of violence to their staff. It is important that where employees' work renders them liable to the threat of violence, employers take reasonably practicable precautions to protect them.

CROWD SAFETY

2.98 In March 1993 HSE published the findings of the RM Consultants' research into crowd behaviour and techniques for managing crowds' safety. The report will interest both social scientists and those whose work involves crowd management issues. HSE also published a free leaflet, *Managing crowds safely*, which summarised some of the main findings of the report. The report will be used as a basis for HSE's own guidelines to be published later. The consultants and HSE took part in a conference on 'Engineering for crowd safety', at which the consultants described their work, and HSE contributed a paper on the legal responsibilities for crowd safety of venue owners and operators.

Chapter 3 ACTION IN PARTICULAR SECTORS

3.1   This chapter reports on activities in particular sectors. It gives:

- a detailed account of work in those sectors which the 1992/93 Plan of Work indicated as being of particular importance; and

- a brief account illustrating the range of activity in other sectors, which are dealt with in alphabetical order.

3.2   The activities reported in the nuclear industry, mines, railways and offshore oil and gas are the responsibility of separate inspectorates within HSE: other sectors are the responsibility of HSE's Field Operations Division (FOD) with the exception of those parts of the leisure and entertainment sector for which local authorities have enforcement responsibilities.

3.3   In particular, the sector reports cover important aspects of the work of the Health and Safety Commission's Industry Advisory Committees (see Annex 1) and HSE's 30 National Interest Groups (NIGs) who support them. The NIGs are centres of expertise within FOD on the health and safety problems of particular sectors; they provide a focus for contacts with those sectors, gather and disseminate information, identify issues and encourage the development of solutions to problems. Central to their work is the preparation, in consultation with their industries, of written guidance and training material on health and safety standards, and the formulation of technical standards to underpin EC directives.

OFFSHORE OIL AND GAS

Safety cases

3.4   Chapter 1 referred to the introduction of the ***Offshore Installations (Safety Cases) Regulations 1992*** which implement recommendations made in Lord Cullen's report on the fire and explosion on the Piper Alpha installation in 1988.

3.5   The preparation and assessment of safety cases will make new demands on both the industry and HSE's Offshore Safety Division (OSD). To help all parties develop the necessary expertise certain operators were invited to submit voluntarily a *'trial' safety case*. Six such voluntary safety cases (VSCs) were received and reviewed by OSD. The experience gained from this exercise has enabled OSD to design the necessary procedures required to handle the large number of safety cases which will be received between May and November 1993.

3.6   The industry too has benefited from this voluntary exercise by gaining a clearer idea of what will be required of an acceptable safety case.

- ***A seminar held in January 1993 to review VSC assessment*** was attended by over 100 industry delegates. This provided an opportunity for extensive discussion at the conclusion of the voluntary exercise and important decisions were reached on the way ahead.

- ***A major public conference was held in Aberdeen*** at the beginning of April 1993 to outline the lessons learned from the VSC exercise, and describe the approach OSD will be taking to safety case assessment.

3.7   Considerable effort has been put into preparing OSD for the receipt and handling of safety cases.

• The Operations Branch in the division has been organised into five operational units, each
including inspection teams, expert teams and a National Responsibility Team (NRT).
Offshore operating companies have been allocated to specific inspection teams so that
industry has a single point of contact with OSD.

• Expert teams inspect particular activities, such as well operations, diving and pipelines.
NRTs act as a focal point within Operations Branch for the development of operational
expertise in particular topics; provide advice, guidance and training for inspectors; and
liaise with industry associations, trade unions and other bodies.

• A major review of the Division's Technology Branch led to its restructuring on 1 April
1993 into four units covering particular discipline areas, a new technology group and a
resources and planning group.

Review of existing legislation

3.8   The Cullen report also recommended that the existing body of offshore safety legislation
should be reviewed and reformed. The Health and Safety Commission announced plans for
this in August 1992; the plans include offshore specific regulations for ***the prevention of
fire and explosion and emergency response; design and construction; and
management and administration***.

3.9   The new regulations will replace existing, largely prescriptive, offshore safety legislation
by more flexible ***goal-setting*** regulations, designed to complement the Offshore Installations

(Safety Case) Regulations 1992 by setting safety objectives which operators and owners of offshore installations will have to achieve in specific areas to underpin the safety case.

3.10 HSE has started informal consultations with industry associations and trade union representatives on the proposed regulations, and discussions to date have been positive and constructive. The consultative document for *the prevention of fire and explosion and emergency response* was issued in September 1993; those for *management and administration* and *design and construction* are planned at the turn of the year, and mid-1994, respectively.

3.11 The review of the *Offshore Installations (Safety Representative and Safety Committees) Regulations 1989* is continuing. The report by the Offshore Study Group of Aberdeen University, on research into the practical working of the regulations, was received in mid-March. The Commission agreed to publish the Aberdeen University Report as a starting point for consultation with all interested parties as HSE develops recommendations to the Commission on any changes needed to the regulations or guidance.

3.12 Proposals are in hand to apply *the Control of Substances Hazardous to Health Regulations (COSHH)* offshore from 1 January 1994. In consultation with the industry, guidance has been developed on how COSHH should apply in the light of the management relationships applying offshore.

3.13 A further recommendation of the Cullen report was that all **standby vessels** should be brought up to a common, acceptable standard. A revised Code of Practice supporting the Offshore Installations (Emergency Procedures) Regulations was issued jointly by HSE and the Department of Transport in July 1991. By 31 December 1992, all standby vessels operating offshore had been certificated as conforming with the new standards.

Guidance

3.14 OSD has been developing its strategy for preparing technical guidance to support the new goal-setting regulations. Guidance will be *non-mandatory*, in line with the recommendations in the Cullen report. OSD has continued to bring forward amendments to the existing *Guidance on the design, construction and certification of offshore installations (Fourth edition)* in a number of priority areas, in particular to emphasise its non-mandatory nature and the need for flexibility.

Research

3.15 A risk based strategy has been developed for the offshore research programme. Advice will be provided by a newly formed Offshore Safety Research Strategy Board chaired by the Chief Executive. Membership of the board reflects participation by the offshore operators, the trade unions, academia, the Certifying Authorities and the Research Councils as well as the key OSD players. The board will focus on prioritising research into offshore health and safety on the basis of assessed risk levels and the potential for research to reduce these levels.

THE NUCLEAR INDUSTRY

3.16 During the year the Nuclear Safety Division (NSD) has continued to concentrate its main efforts on inspection of nuclear sites, assessment of safety cases, particularly for the Sizewell B PWR nuclear power station and, internationally, on the development and

Reactor pile cap

harmonisation of safety standards. Preparatory work has also continued for the Government's proposed review of nuclear power with the preliminary examination of alternative reactor designs.

Assessment of safety cases

3.17 In October 1992 NSD published a new version of the *Safety Assessment Principles* ((SAPs) used by the Nuclear Installations Inspectorate (NII) to assess the safety of nuclear plants. The SAPs are primarily intended as guidance for NII's own assessors but they are also a significant reference point for the industry and public on safety standards. Earlier in October a revised version of *The tolerability of risk from nuclear power stations* (TOR) was published, which explained the basis for HSE's assessments of civil nuclear risks and its approach, as the licensing authority, to their control.

3.18 During the year NII completed assessments on 230 proposals for plant modifications submitted by operators; and issued 155 consents, approvals and agreements. Prominent features of this work included:

- *long term safety reviews (LTSRs) of Magnox plants by licensees.* NII has continued to monitor the implementation across the Magnox stations of safety improvements identified in the early LTSRs. Trawsfynydd was a focus of heavy resource commitment causing some delay in publication of NII's conclusions on other LTSRs;

- after a periodic safety review *Bradwell nuclear power station* resumed operations beyond 30 years after an extensive reactor pressure vessel inspection programme;

- assessment of the *Sizewell B pre-operational safety report* and inspection of the construction and commissioning programme progressed steadily in the run-up to the plant's operation in 1994. Testing and analysis of the computer software for the primary protection system continued. The International Atomic Energy Agency (IAEA) expressed its satisfaction with the pre-operational preparations, including the interface arrangements with HSE as the regulatory body. Initial assessment work began on a derivative design for a Sizewell C power station and on foreign PWRs in preparation for the 1994 review;

- *THORP reprocessing plant:* pre-commissioning safety assessment work continued; and

- the *Torness dry fuel store public inquiry* which took place during December 1992 and January 1993 in Dunbar, focused on NII's safety assessment of the store which Scottish Nuclear Ltd propose to construct at the Torness power station.

Inspection and enforcement

3.19 During the year NII carried out 883 site inspections and witnessed and assessed 44 emergency exercises. Improvement notices were issued by NII for SNL's Hunterston B nuclear power station and to AEA for Windscale Pile 1. BNFL Sellafield was prosecuted for four breaches of nuclear site licence conditions during operation of the Windscale vitrification plant. The company was found guilty on all counts and fined £6000 with costs awarded to HSE.

3.20 The decommissioning of old and redundant plant at nuclear power stations and chemical plant sites assumed greater importance as defuelling proceeded at Hunterston A and Berkeley power stations which have ceased operation, and progress was made in the implementation of the Atomic Energy Authority (AEA) action plans for key sites.

3.21 NII continued to stress the importance of the management of health and safety in the light of changes within the operational organisations of the licensees. Inspectors have in particular focused on the systematic review of licensees' management systems and training arrangements. NII carried out a review of the management of safety arrangements employed by BNFL and UKAEA at their major sites.

3.22 NII has also reviewed its reactor inspection methods and completed a review of licence compliance arrangements for power reactor sites.

3.23 NII is participating in an HSE pilot exercise in Scotland on the release of inspection information by providing quarterly reports on its regulatory activities at the Hunterston nuclear power station to the site's local liaison committee.

Emergency arrangements

3.24 NSD has helped to develop proposals for major changes to off-site emergency arrangements at sites operated by Nuclear Electric. The division also helped in the planning and UK participation in the first OECD/Nuclear Energy Agency international emergency exercise held in March 1993.

International safety standards

3.25 The division has continued its active support of the work of the International Atomic Energy Agency (IAEA), the Organisation for Economic Co-operation and Development (OECD) and the European Communities (EC) through selective participation in various technical projects, forums and seminars. It is now proposed that the IAEA's document *The fundamental principles of nuclear safety*, to which HSE made a substantial contribution, should form the technical basis for an international nuclear safety convention.

3.26 Other contributions to the improvement of international safety standards included:

*   playing a leading role in setting up a Regulatory Assistance Management Group (RAMG) to co-ordinate EC funded aid to the former Soviet Union and countries of Central and Eastern Europe;

*   leading an EC-funded seven-nation consortium, with the chief nuclear regulators from Russia and Czechoslovakia as observers, to advise the Ukraine safety authorities on its regulatory arrangements; and supporting a similar mission to Russia;

*   establishing new bilateral exchanges with the French regulatory authorities to help improve harmonisation of future safety standards; and

*   setting up a formal arrangement with the Japanese nuclear safety authorities for exchange of information.

The Advisory Committee on the Safety of Nuclear Installations (ACSNI)

3.27 ACSNI continued to advise the Health and Safety Commission on its nuclear safety research programme and published its Biennial Report in May 1993. Of particular wider interest was a report *Organising for safety* produced by an ACSNI study group. The report looked at the part organisational factors play in safety and was published in May 1993. The Commission welcomed the report and asked HSE to ensure that its conclusions were publicised beyond the nuclear industry.

Research

3.28 The Health and Safety Commission is responsible for the sponsorship of nuclear safety research and costs are recovered through a levy on the nuclear industry. The research effort covers plant life management (structural integrity), reactor processes, analysis of hypothetical severe accident scenarios, software reliability, human factors and risk analysis. A notable feature of the programme is the significant proportion of collaborative research undertaken with international partners including the CEC, OECD and the United States Nuclear Regulatory Commission.

3.29 In addition, Nuclear Safety Division has a programme of technical support for the Nuclear Inspectorate. The work is carried out under contract by outside bodies and costs are recovered from the licensees. The programme exists to ensure that NII has access to independent technical advice and information to enable the Inspectorate to carry out its regulatory duties adequately.

RAILWAYS

3.30 Chapter 1 (paragraphs 1.64-1.66) described the substantial work undertaken in response to the Government's proposals for the liberalisation and privatisation of British Rail.

Inspection, advice and enforcement

A high speed train, for some 20 years the mainstay of BR's Inter City fleet

3.31 Detailed safety statistics will be included in the Railway Inspectorate's report on railway safety in 1992/93, to be published in early 1994.

3.32 The provisional number of *fatal accidents to railway staff was 11, the lowest ever recorded* and significantly better than the average of 18 for the last five years. Staff most at risk are those who work on the line and nearly 50% of inspection time is devoted to this. The trackside inspection plan for 1992/93 was achieved almost exactly.

3.33 The Railway Inspectorate increasingly called on specialists within HSE to further its investigative and monitoring work. The most far-reaching collaboration was the investigation of train door safety (see paragraph 3.39 below). Other important projects included the investigation of tank wagon axle bearing failures and a quality audit of signalling installation work.

3.34 Inquiries continued during the year into the accident in the Severn Tunnel in 1991. Reports on earlier accidents at *Cannon Street; Chorley Wood; Newton; Hyde Junction* and *Walton on Naze* were published.

New works and technical standards

3.35 Substantial Railway Inspectorate effort was required on the following:

•	the *Manchester Metrolink*, which opened in July 1992;

Testing of the prototype
Sheffield Supertram

- *major inspections of resignalling schemes* at Newcastle, the Great Eastern Line, Cardiff-Maesteg, Chichester-Havant and Paddington were completed;

- *electrification* of the Cambridge to Kings Lynn, Birmingham and the West London lines;

- *work on proposals for new schemes* including - Crossrail, the Jubilee Line Extension, the Heathrow Express Railway and a number of light rapid transit proposals;

- publication in early 1993 of a new section of the Railway Inspectorate's requirements on the *protection of footpath and bridleway level crossings*.

3.36 The Transport and Works Act 1992, introduced by the Department of Transport (DoT), replaced the private bill method of promoting and authorising railway works by a new order-making procedure. Proposed secondary legislation covering the safety approval of new railway works and reporting of incidents was drafted by DoT during the year, in consultation with HSE.

Railway Industry Advisory Committee (RIAC)

3.37 *RIAC's* annual review of *safety management systems* has again helped to identify good practice within the industry. In addition the working party on *trackside safety* continued its research into working practices and began work upon the production of a guide on trackside safety. RIAC also advised the Health and Safety Commission on the conclusions of the *Appleton Report* and provided expert comment during the drafting of the report, *Ensuring safety on Britain's railways.*

Channel Tunnel

3.38 RI has continued to be extensively involved in the work of the **Channel Tunnel Safety Authority** and has played a significant part in the assessment of *Eurotunnel's* proposals for rolling stock and infrastructure (see paragraphs 3.47-3.49 below).

Research

3.39 Work included:

- a report of the study undertaken on behalf of the Health and Safety Commission by Mr Brian Appleton, of the *relative risks of different actions following fire or security alerts on mass transit systems*, which was published in September 1992. Following consideration of the report the Health and Safety Commission offered advice to the Secretary of State for Transport on action that it considered necessary to ensure that the regulation of fire safety on such systems would be based on an all-risks assessment approach;

- publication in May 1992 of HSE's interim report of the investigation of *passenger falls* from British Rail train doors. Agreement was reached with British Rail on a *programme to reduce the risk of persons falling from train doors*. The full report was published in May 1993.

CONSTRUCTION

Safety record

3.40 The *numbers* of fatal, major and over-3-day injuries to employees all continued to fall, with the fatal injury rate showing a reduction for the fifth successive year and non-fatal injury rates likely to be the lowest since RIDDOR was introduced. This may be a reflection of a change in the type of work carried out in the industry in recent years. The injury rates for the self-employed have been less stable, but look likely to be higher for fatal and over-3-day injuries, and slightly lower for non-fatal major injuries in 1992/93 compared with the previous year.

Legislative developments

3.41 In October the Health and Safety Commission issued a *consultative document* on draft *Construction (Design and Management) Regulations (CDM)* and an ACoP to implement the main aspects of the **EC directive** on health and safety at *temporary or mobile construction sites*. There was a generally constructive response to the document in principle although a substantial number of comments on the detail of the proposals have to be taken into account. HSE continued to consult professional groups affected by the regulations and the Commission is expected to consider the final regulations towards the end of the year. There will be separate consultation on draft *Construction (Health, Safety and Welfare) Regulations* to implement Annex IV of the directive.

Inspection, advice and enforcement

3.42 FOD maintained the level of inspectors on construction work during the year and continued to target their inspections on the higher risk activities. Initiatives during the year included:

- *completion of the major national roofwork campaign* mentioned in last year's report: after extensive media publicity HSE inspectors undertook 2500 visits which resulted in considerable enforcement activity. Some 150 prosecutions were taken with fines of up to £20 000 being imposed. A final report on the campaign is being prepared for publication;

- *launch of a health campaign*, which focused on the *use of personal protective equipment*. Information packs containing eight new information sheets on, for example, the protection of the head, hands and feet were issued.

3.43 There were a number of successful prosecutions during the year, including:

- two directors of Henry (Group) Demolition Ltd were convicted when a worker suffered serious burns after striking an underground cable. Both had identified the danger but neither had done sufficient to prevent the accident;

- in London, a director and his company Metro-Rod (London) Ltd were fined £2000 after a worker's leg was injured by a high pressure water jetting gun which the director knew presented a danger;

- Liebherr - Great Britain Ltd, the supplier of an imported tower crane, was prosecuted after a driver fell to his death when a window became displaced. Although later models of the crane were equipped with a safety bar over the window, the suppliers had not informed the users of the earlier versions of the new safety feature. The company was fined £25 000 including costs;

- contractors JFB Construction Ltd were fined £6000 plus costs, when two elderly women fell within an hour of each other, into an inadequately protected excavation in a main road;

- in an incident involving Garside Developments Co Ltd, a demolition worker was killed and two seriously injured when a free standing block wall collapsed on them during high winds. The accident demonstrated the need for careful planning of demolition work and for ensuring the stability of structures as they are demolished.

Consruction Industry Advisory Committee

3.44 The Construction Industry Advisory Committee (CONIAC) maintained its close interest in the progress of the proposed CDM Regulations and continued to develop guidance on health and safety management which is due to be published before the regulations come into force. A working party was set up to oversee parallel guidance on how designers could help to avoid and reduce risks to construction workers.

3.45 In addition:

- a successful *Conference of the Professions*, jointly organised by the Construction Industry Council and HSE, assisted in the consultation process on the draft CDM Regulations and identified more clearly the need for supporting guidance and training for designers and planning supervisors;

- CONIAC submitted *draft guidance* on the *handling of heavy masonry blocks* to the Commission.

Research

3.46 Research into technical and organisational issues is an increasingly important part of HSE's efforts to improve the industry's poor health and safety record. Two projects were completed during the year, which looked at:

- *management and organisational problems* in the light of the proposed CDM Regulations;

- *motivating construction workers to achieve higher standards of safety on site*. A useful method of site safety assessment was developed which will enable health and safety to be monitored more effectively and communicated to the workforce.

Channel Tunnel

3.47 HSE field and specialist inspectors have maintained a vigorous policy of preventive inspection and enforcement in a year which saw rapid progress towards completion of the tunnel project. The Railway Inspectorate, who will have enforcement responsibilities when the Fixed Link becomes an operating railway, have become increasingly involved.

3.48 Particular features of the year included:

- *emphasis on safety management, the control of the construction railway and health hazards* arising from construction activities, including problems with

Track laying in the
Channel Tunnel

diesel exhaust and dust. HSE was involved in a ***simulated emergency exercise*** to test tunnel control room, rescue and emergency service preparations;

- ***co-operation with the French 'Inspection du Travail'*** developed further with several successful joint inspections, in particular of cross-border working conditions. The Channel Tunnel Safety Authority helped both sides exchange information on developments with implications for health and safety. HSE supported the work of the safety authority in many areas, notably consideration of the safety case required for the Fixed Link, of outstanding design questions and of policy on the carriage of dangerous goods; and

- ***a programme of fire trials*** was initiated at the Explosion and Flame Laboratory at Buxton. The purpose was to provide accurate data for comparison with computer predictions of smoke movement in tunnels. The safety authority will consider the results of these tests and other tests being undertaken on fire growth, development and detection in tunnels before making a final decision on the acceptability of the design of the HGV shuttles.

Tunnel accidents and investigations

3.49 October 1992 saw the first fatal accident on the UK side since July 1990. Legal proceedings in respect of this accident have been instituted against Translink Joint Venture, the UK half of the contractors TML. During the year the Crown Court imposed fines on the contractors totalling £90 000 with £35 000 costs in respect of a prosecution following a previous fatality.

AGRICULTURE AND ALLIED INDUSTRIES

Safety record

3.50 The industry as a whole continues to have a high fatal accident rate and it is clear that the large proportion of self-employed who work in the industry suffer higher fatal injury rates than employed persons. Fatal farm accidents include a number involving children who are either resident on the farm or visitors to it. Eight children lost their lives in farm accidents in 1992/93 compared to only two in 1991/92.

3.51 The fragmented nature of the industry and the physical isolation of much of the work has caused Agricultural Inspectors to adopt a threefold strategy to accident and ill-health prevention, summarised as follows:

- seeking to promote ***better design of machinery and plant***;

- ***better advice and training*** and the ***raising of awareness*** of health and safety hazards and risks;

- ***a targeted programme of inspection and enforcement.***

3.52 Several initiatives to raise awareness and improve guidance and standards in the industry were mounted, including:

- production of ***a video and teacher's support pack*** for children on work experience schemes, aimed at raising awareness of the hazards of farming among school-leavers. The video won an award for its class at the European Health and Safety Video Film Festival in Thessalonika, Greece. It is available free to secondary schools;

- ***Festival of Food and Farming held in Hyde Park*** in May 1992. The HSE exhibition stands displayed information about a whole range of activities and particularly the hazards in farming and attracted an estimated 20 000 people. Inspectors also attended national and county agricultural shows providing free information and advice;

- ***designated farms.*** In November 1992, as part of the ***European Year of Health and Safety***, two farm sites were opened to people with a professional interest, to provide an insight into the operation of good farm management practice. The farms, CWS Agriculture Ltd at Farm World, Stoughton, Leicester and Fleckley Grange, Fleckley, Leicester, represented both ends of the scale in agriculture, a large corporation and a small family unit. At Farm World over 14 000 school children visit in organised parties each year;

- ***Farm Wise***, the agricultural equivalent of HSE's successful *Essentials of Health and Safety,* was published in 1993. It was initially distributed free through the trade press to approximately 200 000 people and then issued as a priced publication available from HMSO.

3.53 Work by HSE's three Agricultural National Interest Groups (NIGs) on the development of harmonised European Standards for machinery continued. Other activity to improve

health and safety standards in their sectors included:

- publication of a booklet on the **safeguarding of agricultural machinery** aimed at improving the design of machinery to prevent accidents. This was supported by a seminar for the agriculture industry in 1993;

- **continued research and initiatives by the Crop Production NIG** to reduce accidents at power take off shafts (PTO). There have been eight fatalities at PTO shafts since 1990;

- publication of a free illustrated booklet on the **safe handling and stacking of bales**, as well as free **information sheets** on the **safe use of baling machines and combines**. In these areas of activity there have been 357 reported accidents since 1986, of which 24 were fatal;

- **joint meetings between farmers, machine manufacturers, electricity supply companies and others** organised by the Crop Production NIG to find ways of reducing accidents involving contact with overhead power lines. There have been 45 reported injuries from this source since 1986;

- the **Forestry NIG** has worked closely with training organisations and industry to ensure **minimum acceptable standards of training for users of chain saws.**

Agriculture Industry Advisory Committee

3.54 In March 1993 the Agriculture Industry Advisory Committee (AIAC), which was the first of the Industry Advisory Committees to be set up by the Health and Safety Commission, celebrated its 50th meeting. During 1992/93 the Chemicals in Agriculture Working Group (CHEMAG) considered inter alia, methods of reducing the amount of pesticides used, genetic manipulation, chemical waste disposal, pesticides certificates of competence and the dangers of emissions from the oil seed rape crop. CHEMAG also helped to produce the AIAC publication *A guide to producing a farm COSHH assessment* which provided simple advice on how to comply with the assessment requirements of the regulations.

Research

3.55 During the year there has been considerable publicity about the dangers of and precautions necessary when using sheep dips, particularly those containing organophosphorus compounds. Serious allegations were raised about the use of these materials in various parts of the media and HSE has commissioned further research into their effects on health.

3.56 Following claims that compression sickness has been caused by shallow repetitive diving at fish farms, HSE has sponsored research with University Hyperbaric Research Institute. Depending on the results of the research, advice will be issued to fish farmers and diving contractors.

MINING   Legislative developments

3.57 *Regulations on shafts and winding and explosives* in coal and other safety-lamp mines came into force on 1 April 1993. Extended consultation on the proposed regulations on *management and administration* of safety and health at mines continued throughout the year. In October 1992 revised proposals were submitted to the Health and Safety Commission, who deferred consideration of them until after publication of the Government's White Paper on the future of the coal industry. The Health and Safety Commission eventually considered the proposals in April 1993 and agreed to submit the draft regulations and ACoP to the Secretary of State. The EC *Extractive Industries Directive* (which includes mining), was adopted on 3 December 1992.

Inspection, advice and enforcement

3.58 The number of mines inspectors decreased to 33.5 and there has been further rationalisation of outstation district offices. Overall the staffing of the Division continues to match the level of mining activity. Inspectors carried out 3523 inspections at mines and 318 at other sites taking 1470 mine air and roadway dust samples as part of their work in overseeing environmental standards and protection. Eleven improvement and 20 prohibition notices were issued.

3.59 The Mines Inspectorate published the second in a series of reports on haulage and transport safety, which deals specifically with underground free-steered vehicles. A new advisory working group was also established to review the problems of visibility and cab design for free steered vehicles.

Technical developments

3.60 The Inspectorate supported technical developments both through the industry and HSE's Research and Laboratory Services Division. Projects included:

- *rockbolting.* Three major field trials into the safe use of rockbolts as the sole support for mine roadways were completed during the year. In all the trials, rockbolting provided satisfactory strata control with minimal roof dilation. In addition, the use of rockbolts demonstrated additional safety benefits which should contribute to a reduction in accidents;

- the *measurement and monitoring of radon* in mines and an evaluation of the action that can be taken to reduce exposure;

- the *development of an aerial/transponder man-detection system*, suitable for use in safety-lamp mines, and designed to stop equipment in an emergency on conveyor transport systems.

Accidents and dangerous occurrences

3.61 Six workers were killed and 333 suffered major injury in coal mines in 1992/93. The number of fatalities and major injuries is the *lowest on record* and the 31% reduction in major injuries from the 487 the previous year is very encouraging. Fatal accidents, major injury and over-3-day accident rates have all fallen and the long term trend in total accident rates continues downwards. In non-coal mines there were no fatalities and 13 persons suffered major injuries compared with one killed and ten injured in the previous year.

3.62 Records of dangerous occurrences in coal mines show:

- an *overall decrease* from 160 to 131 mainly due to a reduction in the number of fires and suspected fires from 37 to 14 and ventilation stoppages from 53 to 29;

- underground *locomotive occurrences* increased from 50 to 56. A study of these occurrences indicates the need for more widespread use of track monitoring equipment as an integral part of maintenance;

- *firedamp ignitions* increased from six to eight giving rise to concern. Improved ventilation in the cutting zone and anti-ignition cutting pick design continued.

International mining symposium

3.63 HSE supported a major international symposium held in November 1992 on safety, health and hygiene in mining, organised by the Institute of Mining Engineers. Its aims were directed at fulfilling the objectives of the European Year of Health and Safety and embraced its four main themes: clean air at work; well being at work; safety at work; and measures against noise and vibration.

3.64 The quarrying industry has continued to rationalise its operations in the face of a fall in demand. One hundred and thirty five enforcement notices were served and 14 prosecutions were taken. In one particular case a company director of Chalkman Supplies Ltd was fined £5000 and disqualified from taking up a company directorship for a period of two years for contravening a Prohibition Notice. The company was fined a similar sum and costs totalling £3553 were awarded to HSE. This was the first time that a company director had been disqualified in connection with a health and safety offence.

QUARRIES 3.65 Publicity and initiatives by the Quarries NIG included:

- production of a video aimed at protecting the health of workers exposed to dust - in particular respirable crystalline silica in quarries. The video also gives advice on compliance with the

Control of Substances Hazardous to Health Regulations 1988 (COSHH). In a parallel initiative HSE inspectors carried out an evaluation of the level of understanding of and compliance with COSHH in relation to respirable crystaline silica;

- publication of **Belt and braces**, a report on quarry vehicle accidents which focuses on the need for elevated road edge protection and efficient vehicle braking.

Accidents and dangerous occurrences

3.66 The number of fatal accidents rose from six in 1991/92 to twelve. Seven of these involved vehicles and HSE has dealt with this problem through the *Belt and braces* report and safety seminars. Major injuries fell to 140 compared with 148 in 1991/92 and there has been an overall reduction in accidents. As in previous years a significant proportion of the major injuries were caused by stumbling, falling or slipping. There were nine reported incidents of rock blasted beyond the quarry boundary, five more than the previous year. This rise is disappointing but it is still well below the average of 21 before the Quarry (Explosives) Regulations came into force.

LEISURE AND ENTERTAINMENT

3.67 Local authorities are largely responsible for the enforcement of health and safety in the leisure and entertainment industry, although HSE retains responsibility for a substantial number of premises eg fairgrounds. The leisure industry has become an area of growing importance due to its continuing growth in size and the emergence of new activities and sports.

Guidance has been prepared on health and safety in horse riding establishments

Last year saw a growth in go-kart racing and the increasing elaboration of war/paintball games. In keeping with the changes and developments, HSE continued to develop guidance and advice as follows:

- the *Code of safe practice at fairs* was revised and published as the *Code of safe practice at fairgrounds and amusement parks*;

- guidance on the *use of lasers for entertainment* and on *aerial ropeways* was completed and both will be published in 1993;

- guidance on *pop concert* safety is being prepared jointly with the Home Office and similar guidance is planned for *nightclubs* and *discotheques*;

- draft guidance on *horse riding safety* was finalised and will be published in autumn 1993;

- revision of HSE's joint publication with the Sports Council on *Safety in swimming pools* was started and publication is expected in 1994.

- a Code of Practice on *cable water skiing* was produced with the co-operation of UK operations.

3.68 The European Commission has decided to postpone indefinitely work on the EC directive on *fairground machinery*. Discussions will now be held with other member states to see whether work on the CEN Standard should continue so that a voluntary specification for the safety of fairground equipment can be developed.

OTHER SECTORS 3.69 The following section is intended to give a broad illustration of the range of activity of IACs and NIGs. It does not attempt to list the full extent of work undertaken in each sector. More details of reports on this are submitted annually to HSC, and are available to interested parties. The HSE area office in which the relevant NIG is based can provide further detail about available guidance and other initiatives.

3.70 In many sectors work during 1992/93 focused on:

- the development of industry specific guidance on the new regulations implementing the EC Framework and associated directives (described in Chapter 1); and seminars to promote awareness of them and their implications for the industry;

- initiatives linked to the European Year of Health and Safety; and

- continuing work on the development of European standards.

Ceramics and heavy clay

3.71 The main thrust of the work of the Ceramic Industry Advisory Committee was on the preparation of industry guidance on the Manual Handling Operations Regulations 1992. Lifting, carrying and handling now account for about 40% of reported accidents in the potteries industry; and work related upper limb disorders feature significantly in compensation claims and in complaints to HSE. Accordingly, CERIAC is developing a package of guidance to cover manual handling, seating and posture, and the prevention of work-related upper limb disorders.

Chemicals and glass

3.72 Repair and maintenance of industrial plant often requires access to a section of the plant which has first to be made safe. A permit-to-work (PTW) system is a formal system of communication which is designed to ensure that access to industrial plant only takes place once the plant has been certified as safe. A survey into PTW systems was undertaken by inspectors at 131 chemical companies. In the light of the findings the Chemical Manufacturing NIG is preparing a guidance note on PTW and have also revised their leaflet *Permit-to-work systems*.

Cotton and allied textiles

3.73 The Advisory Committee for the Cotton and Allied Textiles Industry started work on the preparation of guidance for employers on the ***reduction of noise exposure at new machinery***, other than by the use of personal hearing protection.

Crown, fire and police

3.74 The Crown, Fire and Police NIG continued to place emphasis on the importance of effective management of health and safety in its sector, particularly in a series of health and safety seminars for senior Ministry of Defence managers, overseeing a national inspection project on the management of health and safety at establishment level in MOD and preparing for a similar project relating to the rest of the Crown sector in 1993/94.

Diving

3.75 The Diving Operations at Work (Amendment) Regulations 1992 came into force on 17 June 1992. They are intended to improve the safety of diving operations by requiring all diving contractors to register with HSE, clients to notify HSE of all offshore diving operations (where possible, at least 21 days before the operations begin) and prohibiting the use of unregistered diving contractors by clients.

Docks and harbour areas

3.76 Work continued on the proposed revision of the Dangerous Substances in Harbour Areas Regulations 1987. The Docks NIG worked with the International Maritime Organisation to revise their *Recommendations on the safe transport, handling and storage of dangerous substances in port areas*, which is expected to be published next year.

Drinks and packaging

3.77 The NIG continued to seek improvements in the storage and handling of flammable spirit in the scotch whisky industry, and to press for a better awareness of the prevention of fire and explosion. It also examined procedures for reducing the exposure of workers in maltings to dust following the new maximum exposure limit (MEL) for grain dust and published a guidance note to support existing general HSE guidance.

Education services

3.78 The education sector continued to undergo significant management changes. Local authority funded further education and sixth form colleges in England and Wales were preparing for incorporation as independent organisations on 1 April 1993. As independent employers they will in future be wholly responsible for ensuring the health and safety of staff and students.

3.79 The Education Services Advisory Committee (ESAC) published guidance on the *responsibilities of school governors, health and safety management in higher and further education*, and on *inspection, monitoring and auditing*. The latter is the first of three planned guidance booklets aimed at improving health and safety management in all educational premises.

Engineering

3.80 Work of the Engineering NIG included:

- a guidance package prepared by a joint working group on health risks from metal working fluids which has almost been completed and is due to be published in 1993. Dermatitis and related skin complaints are the main hazard but occupational asthma can also occur; and

- a seminar on health and safety standards in the electroplating industry which was held in July 1992, following an enforcement initiative in the industry in 1991. The seminar, which was partly funded by the EC under the EYSHH, was well received and the Metal Finishing Association has asked HSE to participate in similar events throughout the country in 1993/94.

Food

3.81 In view of the high incidence rates of accidents and injuries in the food sector, one of the main aims of the Food NIG during the year was to raise awareness of health and safety in the industry. This was achieved through a main address to the Food and Drink Federation's European Year of Health and Safety Conference with subsequent publications in trade journals. Improved health and safety management was also a priority and the NIG was involved in a number of conferences stressing this theme. Inspection was targeted at employers and firms with a high incidence of accidents and ill health.

Health services

3.82 The Health Services Advisory Committee (HSAC) published its guidance on *safe disposal of clinical waste* and on *manual handling of loads* in the health services. The manual handling guidance was accompanied by a competition pack which was sent to managers in the health care sector so that all could take part. The competition was based on a number of scenarios involving a lifting task and managers were encouraged to organise competitions within their units to coincide with the Workplace Health and Safety Week in November. Over 50 of the best entries went forward to a national competition and prizes, sponsored by industry, were presented to the winners by the Chairman of the Health and Safety Commission at a ceremony held in London. The competition pack was one of two UK entries for the Copenhagen Prize and received an honourable mention at the EYSHH closing ceremony in Copenhagen.

Mineral fibres

3.83 A major new initiative was launched in July 1992 to reduce exposure to *asbestos* dust during the removal of asbestos insulation. A letter was sent to every contractor licensed to do this work informing them of concerns over the lack of progress in the industry towards the use of dust suppression and dust control measures. The initiative is supported by amendments in the revised Approved Code of Practice (second edition) dealing with asbestos insulation removal published in March 1993 requiring improved work methods. A major cause of concern to some contractors has been the risk from heat stress during the removal of insulation from hot plant and pipework. A guidance note on this, entitled *The problems of asbestos removal at high temperatures,* has now been published.

Paper and board

3.84 The Paper and Board NIG has produced three reports for circulation within the industry which will help to form the basis for the development of future guidance. The reports covered the implications of the six-pack regulations, risk assessment in paper mills and manual handling in paper mills. The latter identified a pattern in the cause of manual handling accidents and provided guidance on risk assessment and risk reduction methods.

Plastics, leather and footwear

3.85 A major part of the Plastic, Leather and Footwear NIG's efforts was concentrated on the development of European standards on machinery safety. The NIG also examined ways of disseminating information and guidance to small firms in the footwear industry by:

- helping to set up a small working party under the auspices of the Footwear Joint Industry Safety Committee to produce guidance for small firms on the safe use of solvents;

- organisation, with the help of a reputable shoe manufacturer, of a national seminar on the six-pack regulations which will be held in April 1993.

Printing

3.86 The guidance booklet *Fire safety in the printing industry* was published in a joint initiative by HSE, the Home Office, the Scottish Office and the Printing Industry Advisory Committee (PIAC). The guidance is aimed at improving awareness of fire and explosion risks and outlines practical ways of dealing with these risks.

Public utilities

3.87 In 1992, the Public Utilities NIG organised a number of seminars for trade union officials and safety managers in the water and electricity supply industry, to explain the requirements of the new European legislation and to discuss the implications for the industry.

Rubber

3.88 The Rubber Industry Advisory Committee (RUBIAC) submitted proposals to the Advisory Committee on Toxic Substances (ACTS) for a reduction in the maximum exposure limit for rubber process dust. ACTS accepted the proposal and this was included in the Commission's consultative document on proposals for amendments to the COSHH Regulations which will take effect in January 1994.

Shipbuilding and repair

3.89 The Shipbuilding National Interest Group provide the Secretariat for the Shipbuilding and Ship-repairers Health and Safety Consultative Committee. Activities of the committee included:

- organisation of a poster competition as a contribution to the European Year of Safety, Health and Hygiene. The winning entry adopted the clean air theme; and

- production of guidance on fire safety precautions during the application and removal of foam insulation at gas carriers.

3.90 The NIG also arranged for a video of the BBC television programme 'Fatal Shift' to be made available to the industry. The video illustrates the hazard of oxygen enrichment during work in ships and will be useful as a training aid.

Ship leaving dock

Steelmaking, foundries and molten metals

3.91 In several sectors of the steel industry the general improvement in accident reduction was maintained reflecting its commitment to total quality performance and health and safety training. The involvement of employees in task analysis which seeks to identify risks in the way jobs are undertaken illustrates this. Conditions have improved in the working environment, for example, with substantial investment in extraction systems. Despite the increasing application of modern technology, however, many of the more serious accidents continue to be caused by quite simple and basic failures. In one incident, a contractor broke his back when he fell 20 ft from the unprotected edge of a flat roof. In another, an employee suffered the amputation of three fingers when his hand was trapped in moving rolls while he was attempting to clean them. In both incidents the common features were short term activities and a failure to provide the necessary safeguards. Each incident resulted in a prosecution and a fine of £1000.

3.92 Activities of the Foundries Industry Advisory Committee included:

- publication of advisory leaflets on vibration white finger (VWF); considering the use of vibration damped tools;

- continuing support for research into the potential carcinogenicity of foundry dust and fume;

- reviewing machinery guarding standards and personal protection against molten metal splash.

Woodworking

3.93 The work of the Wood NIG primarily concentrated on:

- improving standards of training of woodworking machinists, including production of a new guidance booklet on *training woodworking machinists*, together with a number of information sheets on safe working practices for those machines which are involved in most accidents;

- participating in the development of European standards for woodworking machines;

- improving communication with the industry through the publication of several Woodworking Information Sheets and a new contact sheet *Wood NIG News*

Wool, clothing and laundries

Good and bad working practices in the woodworking industry

3.94 As part of the *small firms programme*, a leaflet for dry-cleaning companies was published and distributed to over 5000 dry-cleaners. Also in the dry-cleaning sector, the NIG has initiated discussions with interested parties on the re-introduction to this country

of machines using flammable hydrocarbon solvents. These are of particular interest to companies dealing with more delicate materials such as leather, in view of the impending phase-out of chlorofluorocarbon solvents under the Montreal Protocol. The NIG is preparing guidance for users and suppliers of these machines and is taking a close interest in the installation of the first machine.

Chapter 4 MANAGING HSE

4.1   The Health and Safety Executive - a body of three people appointed by the Health and Safety Commission with the approval of the Secretary of State for Employment - advises and assists the Commission in its functions. The Executive's staff of some 4500 include inspectors, policy advisers, technologists and scientific and medical experts. They are collectively known as HSE. A detailed breakdown of HSE staff is at Annex 7. They are widely dispersed geographically with four main HQ locations (London, Bootle, Aberdeen and Sheffield), 21 Area Offices and some 20 other offices.

4.2   The management of HSE involves the discharge of three main types of work.

- *Policy*. The policy branches advise the Health and Safety Commission on the need for changes in legislation or standards. Their work includes negotiations on European Community proposals and liaison with a wide range of national and international organisations. They depend for their expertise on advice from and close liaison with staff carrying out the other types of work.

- *Operations*. Operational staff inspect industrial activity, give advice, investigate accidents and enforce compliance with legal requirements and reasonable standards. The great majority of such staff are in the Field Operations Division which brings together the Factory, Agriculture and Quarries Inspectorates, the doctors and nurses of the Employment Medical Advisory Service, and specialist inspectors and scientists in Field Consultancy Groups. The remainder are in separate divisions covering Railways, Mines, Nuclear Installations and Offshore Safety. The latter two divisions deal with policy as well as operational issues for their respective industries.

- *Technological, scientific and medical*. These staff supply technological, scientific and medical back-up to other parts of HSE and to Government on industrial health and safety matters, including the extent and nature of risks, the effects of hazards on individuals or the environment, and appropriate standards. They play a vital part in operational activity, in the making of safety standards, often in international negotiation, and the assessment of safety cases for nuclear and major hazards installations.

ORGANISATIONAL CHANGE

4.3   The chart over shows the organisational structure of HSE at April 1993.

4.4   Last year's report described the build up of staff and support systems in Offshore Safety Division which transferred to HSE from the Department of Energy in April 1991, the major reorganisation of policy divisions and the setting up of the Research Strategy Unit (see paragraph 4.49 below).

4.5   During 1992/93 a *Risk Assessment Policy Unit* was set up in HSE. Its main aims are to:

- promote a coherent and consistent approach to risk assessment in HSE;

- develop and promote HSC/E's approach in industry, other departments and agencies dealing with safety issues, the EC and other national and international fora;

- further the understanding and acceptability of risk assessment and its application; and

- promote strategies for research and improve communications on risk assessment.

HSE organisation

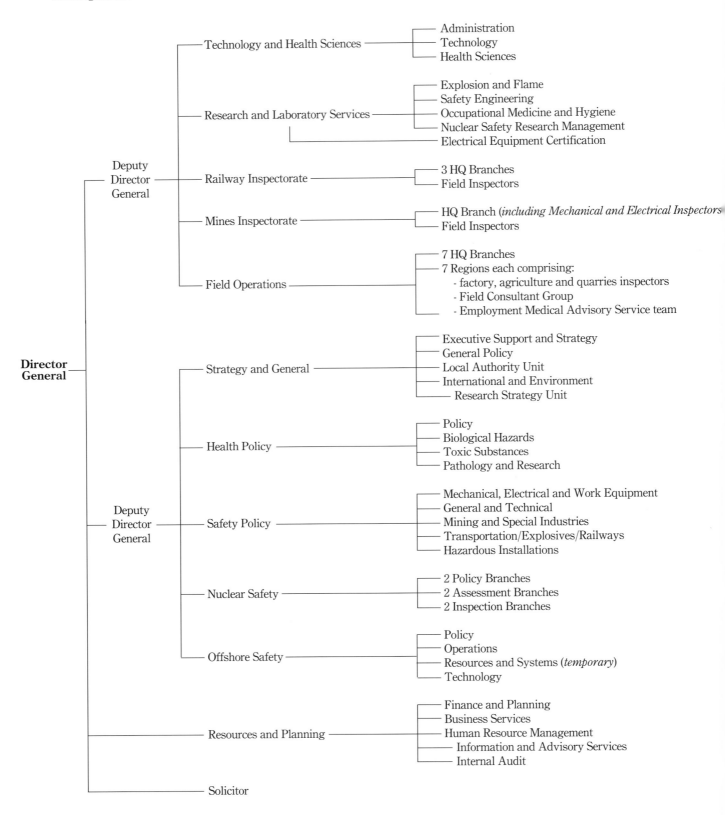

Progress on developing the use of risk assessment as a tool for prioritising action to reduce risk is described in paragraphs 1.31-1.35.

4.6   A study by PA Consulting Group, mentioned in the 1992/93 Plan of Work, concluded that on balance the *Electrical Equipment Certification Service* (EECS) should be put into the private sector, preferably by selling it as a going concern. Legal advice was sought on whether Ministers or the Health and Safety Commission had the power to sell EECS in this way. It was concluded that privatisation would require primary legislation and Ministers announced in April 1993 that they would be seeking Parliamentary approval for the necessary enabling powers.

PLANNING AND FINANCIAL MANAGEMENT

4.7   Progress was made during the year on improving planning and financial management. Measures included the following:

•   discussions were initiated with the Employment Department on revision of HSE's Memorandum of Financial Arrangements, defining conditions attached to HSE's grant-in-aid, and HSE contributed fully to an initiative launched by the ED Group headquarters to improve financial control arrangements throughout the Group;

•   further steps were taken to improve the professionalism and competency of those with budget responsibilities within HSE's devolved financial management system. Two workshops were held for divisional Finance Managers (FMs) and a survey of FMs training needs was completed;

•   an *Operators' guide to devolved budgeting*, providing a comprehensive definition of roles and responsibilities and budget guidance, was finalised;

•   the overall divisional budget structure and the responsibilities of budget holders and FMs were reviewed and steps taken to improve auditing of divisional finance arrangements; and

•   attention was focused on efficiency improvements, including by issuing a leaflet to all HSE staff entitled *HSE resources: how you can help save money*.

4.8   A project to Computer Aid the Planning System (CAPS) was launched in April 1992 to improve financial information systems and maximise the benefits of information technology for HSE's planning and financial management systems. An improved efficiency monitoring system is now operating (see paragraph 4.13 below) and an enhanced system for providing and monitoring the information required by the Public Expenditure Survey is under development.

IMPROVING VALUE-FOR-MONEY

Performance measures

4.9   Selected output and performance measures (OPMs) are set out in Annex 5. They are drawn from a larger set of measures used within HSE to assess output, activities and efficiency. A Treasury report on HSE's performance measures, produced in September 1992, made recommendations on improving HSE's current OPMs and on the use of new measures, including financial measures and other business ratios. The report formed the basis for work over the past year to further improve HSE's OPMs, including measures of quality, timeliness, achievement of objectives within timetable and budget and response to customers, in particular the public.

4.10 The output and performance measures included in Annex 5 indicate:

- many areas of activity rose in 1992/93, including Field Operations Division advisory contacts, investigations of complaints from workers and the public, and visits in support of special health and safety projects and campaigns. Planned inspections by specialist, nuclear and offshore inspectors rose, as did standards work and some demand-led certification, approval and assessment work (including nuclear consents and approvals, railway fixed works and rolling stock submissions and approvals, work related to new substances, jobs completed by the Electrical Equipment Certification Service and offshore safety cases - where a peak of activity is still to come);

- there were significant increases in publications activity, including technical guidance documents, and in most measures of HSE's interactions with the public (enquiries from the public, correspondence, press notices and conferences, exhibitions and displays). Research acitivity also increased;

- a small reduction in Field Operations Division planned inspections, partly as a result of redeploying resources to train new recruits, and because of a need to meet other demands on inspectors including the investigation of more complaints, the need to advise on new EC-based legislation and work in support of the European Year of Health and Safety. Inspections have become more protracted owing to a commitment to target sites and activities which present the greatest risk and to changing inspection techniques which seek to maximise the effectiveness of the inspection programme. Where other indicators are falling this is mainly because activities are demand-led (eg asbestos and petroleum licence approvals, Mines Inspectorate activity which is broadly contracting in proportion to the decline in the industry). In some cases policy decisions have been taken to switch resources, for example medical assessment work has reduced, while advisory visits by field medical and nursing staff have increased.

4.11 Although these measures demonstrate effort directed towards major areas of activity they are by no means the whole of HSE's output and performance. In particular, they cannot indicate the degree to which HSE is called on to react to unforeseen events of every magnitude and at every level. Nor do they reflect the diversity of activities such as inspections, licence monitoring, accident investigations and safety case assessments, which are not standard items. The effort required may range from half an hour to many weeks.

Efficiency gains

4.12 HSE planned to make specific and costed efficiency gains equivalent to 1.71% of running costs in 1992/93, against Treasury expectations of 1.5% of running costs. Actual achievement was 1.74% for the whole of HSE including the Nuclear Installations Inspectorate (NII), as shown in the table below. These follow gains of 1.57% in 1990/91 and 1.73% in 1991/92, and are all new gains. In 1992/93 the largest contributions stemmed from IT investment, improvements in organisation and work allocation and savings from improved purchasing procedures.

4.13 A new database tracking system was brought into use during the year, which has improved the tracking and monitoring of efficiency savings.

Costed gains in efficiency made in 1992/93 (p)

Nature of efficiency gain	Target £000	Outturn £000
1 Additional frontline work by inspectors resulting from action to simplify office and administration procedures, better work planning, use of information technology etc	440	1021
2 Additional output and cash saving from investment in IT, saving staff time either in posts retrenched, or released to absorb other tasks	898	463
3 Improved administrative procedures; reorganisation/ rationalisation/staff grading changes	277	25
4 Savings from the implementation of management services reviews	34	12
5 Savings from improved procedures for purchasing running cost goods and services	321	593
6 Savings from investment in, and better control of, telecommunications	51	11
7 Savings in expenditure on travel	0	61
8 Miscellaneous including building/accommodation savings, energy efficiency	618	214
Total	2639	2628
% Running costs		1.74
9 Savings by NII (shown separately as NII's running costs are 'ring fenced'): additional inspector output from use of IT	159	160
%NII running costs		1.36

p provisional

Major reviews

4.14 All non-departmental public bodies, such as the Health and Safety Commission (HSC) and HSE, are subject to comprehensive review at least every five years, when the continued justification for their existence and their systems of financial management and control are examined. The Employment Department completed a quinquennial review of HSC and HSE in 1992. Their report recommended, among other things:

- that there is a continuing need for HSC and HSE;

- that the structure of a number of HSE divisions should be reviewed;

- a wide ranging market testing programme;

- a review of HSE's management committee structure; and

- a number of detailed improvements to the planning and financial control systems.

All of the recommendations are either now implemented, in the process of being implemented, or require action at a later date.

4.15 In October 1992 the National Audit Office began a value-for-money study of HSE. The NAO intended to consider how HSE:

- identifies risks to health and safety;

- promotes awareness of legislation;

- encourages compliance with legislation;

- directs and undertakes inspection and other compliance work to establish whether health and safety requirements are met; and

- seeks to remedy non-compliance.

A final report is to be sent to the Controller and Auditor-General in November 1993.

Evaluation and effectiveness studies

4.16 There was a marked increase during the year in evaluation work across HSE, including studies to measure the effectiveness of *policies* (for example, the Diving Operations at Work (Amendment) Regulations 1992, and the Construction (Head Protection) Regulations 1989) and *activities* (for example, notices given to employers about health and safety systems, investigations into incidents of material or mechanical failure and all mainstream research projects). Advice to those carrying out evaluation studies has been improved and an HSE video will soon be made available to staff involved in this work.

Market testing

4.17 HSE's market testing programme for 1992/93 included the following services:

- graphics

- print unit

- distribution of publications

- estates management

- typing, messenger, security and central despatch services at HQ sites.

4.18 The 1992/93 programme covered work valued at some £11 million and 225 staff units. The contract for the distribution of publications was awarded to Prolog and Dillons in summer 1993; invitations to tenders for the graphics service were issued in September 1993. Feasibility studies have been completed for most of the remaining services in the programme. A team with responsibility for market testing has been set up and work is progressing both on the programme and on a range of guidance for managers and staff.

4.19 Part 1 of a market testing study covering HSE's core regulatory functions, including inspection, was delivered to Ministers. In responding to the Chairman of the Commission, Ministers noted the views that contracting out most of the core regulatory functions would be technically possible, but that important risks and drawbacks would need to be weighed in the balance. They reserved judgement until the second stage of the study had been completed.

Information technology

4.20 Progress has been made with the implementation of HSE's second five-year information strategy. Main achievements in 1992/93 included:

- letting the contract for the modern computers on which HSE's new field operations system (FOCUS) will operate. FOCUS aims to provide a comprehensive, national source of information about the people and organisations HSE deals with, and about the work of field staff in achieving better standards of health and safety. The development and delivery of the software and a comprehensive staff training programme is now underway. The new system is due to become operational in April 1994;

- commissioning and developing the databases for handling and analysing the complex information required under the new offshore safety case regime. The new system will come into operation in 1993/94;

- implementing an HSE-wide purchasing system (PURPOSES: see paragraph 4.25 below);

- conducting a review of the organisation's communications needs (including telephone, data, fax, video). The report will identify the facilities needed and recommend how they should be provided to secure effective communications at the most competitive price; and

- taking an important step forward in converting HSE's information technology so that it is based on standards which several suppliers can meet. A number of the new IT systems introduced during the year, eg for purchasing, and a number of major systems currently being developed, eg FOCUS and the databases for Offshore Safety Division, run under the UNIX operating system.

4.21 The growth in IT activity in the past three years is illustrated by the following figures:

	1990/91	1991/92	1992/93
Ratio of workstations to HSE staff units	2.8	2.3	1.9

Purchasing

4.22 HSE has continued to enjoy the benefits, both in quality and value for money, of those contracts centrally negotiated by the Directorate of Purchasing and Supply (DPS) during the last two years. Further areas were identified during the year for central contracts, including electrical components and laboratory consumables.

4.23 The development of professionalism in purchasing has been pursued with five members of DPS staff achieving success in the Foundation Stage examinations of the Chartered Institute of Purchasing and Supply, with one going on to gain full professional membership. HSE Area Office purchasing procedures were developed and implemented through residential training courses run in conjunction with the University of Ulster.

4.24 During the year DPS built up a specialist group to provide advice and assistance across HSE on EC procurement requirements and also recruitment of external consultants. DPS worked closely with the market testing team (see paragraph 4.17 above) in drawing up specifications, advertising and tendering procedures (particularly those relevant to the EC Procurement Directives), analysis of tenders and the subsequent award of contracts.

4.25 PURPOSES, the HSE-wide computerised purchase order, stock control and asset recording system, was partially implemented during the year and will be fully operational throughout HSE by the end of December 1993. It will achieve better value for money for the goods and services HSE buys and will also ensure compliance with new EC procurement legislation.

4.26 The Executive is committed to the principle of prompt payment for suppliers' bills and monitors performance to determine the percentage of bills paid within the agreed period of credit or within 30 days where no credit period has been agreed. During the year sampling showed that 94% of bills were paid within the agreed period, an improvement on the previous year's figure of 86.6%.

Internal Audit and Management Services

4.27 Following approval by the HSE Audit Committee (which oversees the privatisation of audit work) of a broadening of the scope of Internal Audit's activity to cover, for example, auditing the efficiency and effectiveness of frontline operations such as inspections, a number of diverse audits were undertaken during the year including: nuclear safety assessment; costing, charging and accounting for HSE services; offshore research; and trading accounts. Internal Audit reported on the computerised purchasing system delivered during the year (see paragraph 4.25 above) and established arrangements to participate from the feasibility stage in HSE's accounting system replacement project. They also provided advice to management on some of the issues raised by market testing (see paragraph 4.17 above).

4.28 The Management Services team completed nine projects on behalf of a range of HSE clients. These included a management review of the Railway Inspectorate, an assessment of the training needs of Offshore Safety Division and an organisational review of Field Operations Division HQ. Extensive support was provided for the development of a computer aided job evaluation system for the HSE Pay and Grading Review.

Total Quality

4.29 The principles of Total Quality (TQ) have been applied throughout HSE, but not in a prescriptive manner. Divisions have developed TQ practices to suit their own particular needs and circumstances. In the main, attention has been paid to building quality into everyday working processes, instead of considering TQ as a separate issue. Examples of quality initiatives include the following:

- the development by Field Operations Division, described in paragraph 1.6, of a monitoring tool to enable judgements to be made about the most effective inspection techniques;

- improved communications in Research and Laboratory Services Division, with the introduction of a Divisional newsletter, a more open style of Divisional management meetings and a new style of Annual Conference open to all staff; and

- a review by Technology and Health Sciences Division of the processes used for handling applications for approval of Radiation Dosimetry Services, which resulted in significant reductions in the time taken to process applications.

4.30 HSE is represented on a cross-departmental TQM consortium and HSE's Total Quality club continues to meet quarterly, acting as a networking focal point for all divisions to learn from each others initiatives.

HUMAN RESOURCE MANAGEMENT

Recruitment and retention

4.31 Total HSE staffing increased from 4321 on 1 April 1992 to 4537 on 1 April 1993. The need for the increase was partly a legacy of HSE's difficulties in recruiting and retaining staff during the period 1987-1989, but mainly to ensure adequate resourcing of the many new areas of work taken on in the last decade. The main areas of expansion were:

- *Offshore Safety Division.* The major recruitment effort for OSD continued, to enable the Division to take forward the major new tasks arising from Lord Cullen's report on the Piper Alpha oil rig disaster. However, there was a significant decrease in the number of applications for vacant posts and as a result total staffing was 12 below the target of 332 on 1 April 1993. In particular, there was a shortfall of 17 on the target for offshore inspectors, although a further seven inspectors joined the division early in 1993/94;

- *Railway Inspectorate.* The number of inspectors in RI rose from 27 to 35, three short of the revised target. The increase enabled the Inspectorate to devote more staff resources to its existing work programme, while ensuring that sufficient effort was allocated to safety and security on the Channel Tunnel railway. A further increase in the number of inspectors has now been approved to handle additional work arising from the rail privatisation programme (paragraphs 1.64-1.66);

- *Factory Inspectorate.* Rebuilding FI levels continued during 1992/93 and staffing rose over the year from 634 to 658 on 1 April 1993. The autumn 1992 recruitment campaign was extremely successful and those who were accepted took up post in spring and summer of 1993.

4.32 The success of the various recruitment exercises, although due in part to the effects of the recession, reflect improvements arising from the decision to arrange more exercises in-house. With the exception of the major Factory Inspectorate exercise, all recruitment is now handled by HSE's personnel staff. This has led to improvements in speed of response and has allowed divisions much greater involvement in the selection process. Where necessary, external specialist agencies have been contracted, particularly for offshore specialists, and HSE will continue to exploit the greater recruitment flexibilities now available.

4.33 Although the number of staff who left HSE showed an increase over the previous year more than 60% were retirements. Underlying wastage is otherwise declining.

Pay and grading

4.34 HSE started a review of pay and grading early in 1992 to consider how it could best respond to the Government's policy of encouraging departments to take greater responsibility for pay and grading matters. The review team have recommended that HSE seek fully delegated powers to conduct pay bargaining and that it conducts a major job evaluation exercise to establish a new grading structure. Work is continuing on how to implement these recommendations and a business case will be presented to HM Treasury in due course.

Equal opportunities

4.35 HSE is committed to equality of opportunity for all its staff, irrespective of gender, marital status, ethnic origin, religious belief, age, sexual orientation or disability. The continuing implementation of a four-year equal opportunities action programme is a clear indication of this commitment. The programme includes specific action designed to eliminate discrimination and to encourage positive action initiatives. Examples of initiatives during 1992/93 were:

- recruitment measures to target applications from under-represented groups, particularly ethnic minorities and women specialists;

- the presentation of equal opportunities training and awareness events in various divisions and locations; and

- extension of the network of Sexual Harassment Advisers - confidential counsellors who are available to offer advice and support.

4.36 HSE's equal opportunities policies are supported by the development of child care facilities and a project is currently under way to assess demand in each HSE office.

HRD strategy

4.37 HSE continued to give priority to its Human Resource Development (HRD) Strategy, now in its fourth year of operation. During the year, HSE's staff training and human resources development functions were combined to form an integrated Staff Development and Training command. This recognises the important role which training plays in staff development.

4.38 A wide range of activities were used by divisions to develop the competence of staff in line with operational needs. There was a significant increase in the number of staff secondments to outside organisations in the public and private sector, and an increase in secondments to the European Commission where a number of HSE experts worked on health and safety directives important to the United Kingdom. Valuable secondments were also arranged to Expo '92 in Seville, the Economic Summit and 10 Downing Street. Many staff benefited from opportunities for project work and short-term attachments in other HSE divisions.

4.39 Within the HRD Strategy, management development received particular attention. The Senior Management Development Programme provided further support for developmental activities, such as study for Masters of Business Administration by distance learning and team building events to help managers lead organisational change. The management standards developed by the Management Charter Initiative, the lead body on management qualifications under the National Council for Vocational Qualifications, have been introduced to improve performance at junior management levels.

4.40 New Career Planning Review Groups have been set in place to strengthen career planning at senior levels in HSE. Considerable progress has been made in the development of 'compacts' which will clarify the respective roles of central management and individual divisions in personnel matters.

Staff training

4.41 The continuing recruitment, particularly in Offshore Safety Division, together with recent substantial intakes of new inspectors elsewhere in HSE, meant that over £1.3 million was spent on training new inspectors and specialists, 57% of the central training budget. The introductory course was restructured into a new Foundations of Health and Safety course at Loughborough University after a competitive tender. The Diploma course in health and safety, taken by all new factory and agricultural inspectors, was put to tender and Aston University, who were already running it, were awarded the new contract.

4.42 Other examples of training provided during the year included the following:

• a wide range of technical, legal, professional and information technology courses were run to maintain and improve the in-service skills of HSE staff. A particular priority was helping staff in the Field Operations Division prepare for the introduction of FOCUS (see paragraph 4.20 above);

• HSE has initiated a pilot programme aimed at developing a selection of staff to achieving National Vocational Qualifications (NCVQ) in Business Administration, Assessment and Management at appropriate levels. Training courses are being reviewed to ensure compatibility with national standards;

• managerial and developmental training opportunities continued to be expanded with training available to staff not only in the training centres in Bootle, London and Sheffield, but also in HSE regions; and

• a further programme of language skills training was provided to assist the work of negotiating and influencing in EC and other international organisations.

4.43 Training activity remained high with the number of courses mounted increasing to 906, 35% more than the previous year's total.

Staff training activity

	1990/91	*1991/92*	*1992/93*
Total training days	21720	28468	33723
Training days per 1000 staff in post	5542	6797	7651
Total trainees	8409	8769	11476
Trainees per 1000 staff in post	2145	2094	2604
Courses run by HSE's Training Section	388	672	906

GREEN HOUSEKEEPING AND ENERGY CONSERVATION

4.44 HSE has signed a declaration to a 'Corporate Commitment' which ensures that the organisation plays its part in implementing the initiatives set out in the Government's White Paper 'This Common Inheritance'.

4.45 In 1992/93 HSE issued an Environmental Policy Statement to all members of staff and various projects have been undertaken, including:

- the introduction of a system to collect waste paper and send it for re-cycling (known as the 'Green Bin' scheme);

- the collection of aluminium cans for re-cycling;

- participation in the Government Energy Efficiency Campaign which has led to a reduction in consumption levels; and

- the establishment of a network of Energy Wardens to ensure that good housekeeping measures are practiced.

RESEARCH

4.46 Each year, HSE spends about £38m directly on research in support of its science and technology objectives. During 1992/93 about £8.5m was devoted to in-house research into occupational health and safety. The internal programme, in addition to meeting specific needs for information also sustains a core of scientific expertise to assist, for example, with forensic investigations and provide the expertise needed for the technical management of extramural projects.

4.47 The bulk (about 80%) of the expenditure is extramural and at any time there will be about 800 projects involving some 230 different contractors. The market testing study, referred to in paragraph 4.17, includes an examination of the proper balance between the internal and external programmes.

4.48 The Research Committee, comprised of HSE senior management, maintains an overview of the programmes and sets a strategy for HSE research. In 1992/93 the extramural programme was made up as follows:

Occupational safety, hygiene and health	£7.2m - 265 projects
Offshore safety	£6.7m - 241 projects
Nuclear safety	£11.4m - 163 projects
Support to the Nuclear Installations Inspectorate	£2.3m - 89 projects
Agency agreement with the National Radiological Protection Board	£0.3m - 23 projects
Totals	£27.9m - 781 projects

The costs of the nuclear safety and support to the Nuclear Installations Inspectorate are recovered from the industry.

4.49 The Research Strategy Unit works with the offshore and nuclear research management teams to ensure a coherent overall programme with maximum cross-fertilisation of ideas and minimum duplication of effort. During 1992 HSE convened a series of subject research groups to focus on important research topics, for example, risk assessment, gas explosions and occupational health. Each group reviewed previous and current HSE research on its topic and advised on what future research was needed to assist in meeting HSC/E's priorities and

RLSD's new Robens
Building on the
Sheffield site

objectives. This advice will assist in judgements on the apportionment of resources between the various hazards that research must address.

4.50 HSE continues to make full use of the market when commissioning research. Most nuclear safety research has been done in the past by the Atomic Energy Authority (AEA), but HSE has been widening the contractor base to include university departments, private consultants and other research organisations. About 5% of nuclear safety research was non-AEA in 1991/92 and this increased to 14% in 1992/93. For 1992/93, the Agency Agreement with the Safety and Reliability Directorate of the AEA was replaced by a call-off contract by which work could be commissioned on demand. This contract has been put to competitive tender for work required from April 1993. The research undertaken by the National Radiological Board is also being commissioned by a call-off contract during 1993.

New Occupational Medicine and Hygiene Laboratory

4.51 A new laboratory has been built adjacent to HSE's existing facilities in Sheffield to house staff of the Occupational Medicine and Hygiene Laboratory, originally located in Cricklewood, London. The move means that all the work of HSE's Research and Laboratory Services Division on occupational medicine and hygiene is now carried out on the one site, with consequent improvements in efficiency and effectiveness.

4.52 The new laboratory, which was opened in October 1992 by HRH The Prince Phillip, Duke of Edinburgh, has some of the finest research facilities of their kind in Europe. It is housed in the Robens Building, named after Lord Robens who, as Chairman of the Committee on Health and Safety at Work, was instrumental in establishing the 1974 Act which created the Health and Safety Commission and Executive. Lord Robens attended the opening ceremony.

PART II
Statistics

INTRODUCTION

1   This year's Statistical Report includes the seventh set of figures since the RIDDOR reporting system was introduced in 1986. It contains a summary of the key statistics; more detailed figures on both injuries and occupational ill health are included in a new Statistical Supplement.

2   The report is principally based on RIDDOR statistics, but also draws on data from other sources, most notably for occupational diseases for which the RIDDOR figures provide a very incomplete picture. The use of other sources of information on *fatalities* in addition to RIDDOR ensures that statistics on fatalities are virtually complete. However it is possible that a small number of fatalities, mainly to members of the public, may be missed due either to the particular circumstances of the accident or a lengthy gap between the accident and the ensuing fatality. This should not affect the consistency of the series over time.

3   As usual, the RIDDOR statistics for the latest year are provisional (denoted by 'p' in the tables). Final figures are normally about 2.5% higher overall because of late reports and because fatalities include deaths up to a year after the date of an accident. To help interpretation, broad estimates of the final injury *rates* have been included, and where possible these are reflected in the commentary. Table A compares the provisional rates for each of the main sectors with the estimated final rates. The detailed tables of numbers of injuries and injury rates are of necessity based on the provisional figures.

Table A   Injury incidence rates (per 100 000 employees): provisional figures compared with the best estimated final results, by main industrial sector

Sector	1992/93p			1992/93 ef		
	Fatal	*Major*	*Over-3-day*	*Fatal*	*Major*	*Over-3-day*
Agriculture, forestry and fishing	7.1	162.4	548.2	7.8	165	558
Energy and water supply industries	4.9	193.9	1617.6	4.9	194	1640
Manufacturing	1.4	123.4	1104.7	1.4	125	1120
Construction	7.3	239.5	1356.0	7.5	241	1368
Services	0.6	50.9	460.7	0.7	53	479
All industry	1.2	78.8	659.5	1.3	81	677

p   provisional   ef   best estimate of final results

4   In contrast to the comprehensive information available on fatalities, a supplement to the 1990 Labour Force Survey (LFS) confirmed HSE's previous concerns that *non-fatal injuries* are significantly under-reported. The supplement revealed that only a third of reportable non-fatal injuries to employees are being reported, with marked variations between industrial sectors (from under a fifth in agriculture and only a quarter in the services sector to two fifths in manufacturing and construction and four fifths in the energy sector). For the self-employed, only one in twenty of reportable injuries are reported. Thus while the provisional non-fatal injury rate for 1992/93 for injuries to employees reported under RIDDOR was 740 per 100 000 employees, the estimated total level of reportable injuries was 2300 per 100 000 employees with rates varying across the main industry sectors from 2000 in services to 3100 in manufacturing, 3500 in construction and 3800 in agriculture. This report therefore concentrates on fatal injuries.

5   Two key features emerged from the LFS research. First, reported accidents are a good indicator of the relative order of risks by industry. Second, the physical types of injury in reported accidents are representative of those indicated by the survey. This means that reported injuries, though incomplete, still reflect the overall picture of all accidents in terms of relative risks and physical injuries.

6   A further set of questions on work-related injuries is to be asked in the 1993/94 LFS and thereafter on a regular basis. These questions will provide a global figure for injuries including those not reportable under RIDDOR. They will also provide the opportunity to examine any changes in the level of reporting, although it is thought unlikely that reporting patterns have influenced the trends in non-fatal rates.

7   The LFS Supplement provides the most comprehensive picture we have of the extent of work-related ill health and revealed that about 6% of adults who have ever worked suffer some form of ill health which they believed was caused or made worse by their work. Trends in this report are limited largely to the compensated (or prescribed) diseases and are thus affected by changes in the propensity to claim benefit as well as the, often lengthy, time lags between exposure and the onset of symptoms of the disease.

KEY INJURY STATISTICS AND TRENDS

Overview

The fatal injury rate for 1992/93 is likely to be the lowest ever reported. Part, but not all of this reduction, is due to changing patterns of employment.

8   The number of fatal injuries to employees and the overall fatal injury rate in 1992/93 have dropped to the lowest levels ever reported. The final fatal injury rate for all employees in 1992/93 is expected to be 1.3 per 100 000 employees. However the fall in the rate largely reflects changes in the pattern of employment with a shift away from the higher risk industries into the generally lower risk service sector. In both the construction and manufacturing sectors, the final fatal injury rates are expected to continue to fall. In the energy and agricultural sectors, the rates are more likely to fluctuate because these areas account for small proportions of employees and hence relatively few injuries. There was a marked fall in the fatal injury rate in the energy sector in 1992/93. In agriculture, the fatal injury rate was higher in 1992/93 than in the previous year, but is likely to be around the average for the last six years on finalisation. In the service sector, the fatal injury rate remained at virtually the same level as in the last six years. There were similar trends in the non-fatal major and over-3-day injury rates in the different sectors.

Figure 1 Fatal injury rates by SIC80 division 1986/87 to 1992/93 estimated finals

Figure 2 Non-fatal injury rates by SIC80 division 1986/87 to 1992/93 estimated finals

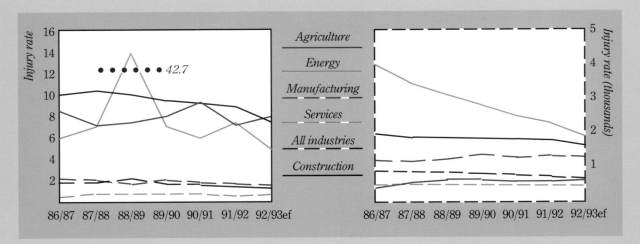

Employees

9   Figure 3 shows how employee fatal injury rates, and numbers of injuries for employees, have changed over the last 30 years. Despite some extension of the requirement to report fatalities, rates in the late 1980s and early 1990s are generally less than a quarter of those at the beginning of the 1960s and less than half those at the beginning of the 1970s.

The final fatal injury rate for 1992/93 is expected to be 1.3 per 100 000 employees. This is the third successive year in which the fatal injury rate has shown a reduction.

10   The final *fatal* injury rate for 1992/93 is expected to be 1.3 per 100 000 employees, based on the 249 fatal injuries to employees provisionally reported which are expected to reach about 265 when the final figures are available. This would be both the *lowest rate* and the *lowest number of fatalities* ever reported. This is the third successive year in which the fatal incidence rate has fallen and the fatal injury rate is now about 20% lower than in the mid-1980s.

Figure 3   Fatal injuries to employees. Injury incidence rates 1961 to 1992/93p

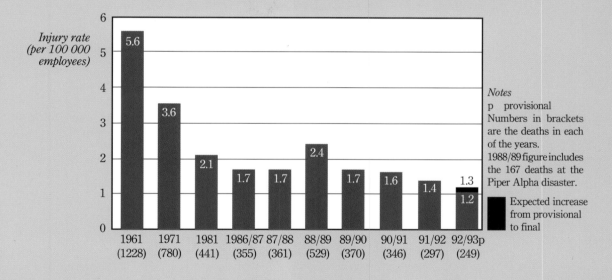

Notes
p   provisional
Numbers in brackets are the deaths in each of the years.
1988/89 figure includes the 167 deaths at the Piper Alpha disaster.

Expected increase from provisional to final

11   Since the mid-1980s there have been a number of important changes in the pattern of employment. For example, employment in the coal industry in 1992/93 was one third of the level in 1986/87 and the numbers of people employed in both manufacturing and construction rose to a peak in the late 1980s and have since dropped by over 15%. In contrast employment in the service industries increased steadily in the late 1980s rising by 10% between 1986/87 and 1990/91 with slight decreases in each of the last two years.

12   In the main, these changes away from high risk industries towards the lower risk service sector should lead naturally to a lower overall rate. A crude assessment of whether the change in employment mix has been responsible for the decline in the overall rate can be made by applying the 1986/87 incidence rates to numbers employed in the different industrial classes for each year since 1986/87. Although the shifting employment pattern is a significant contributory factor to the fall in the fatal injury rate, it does not account for all of the decrease.

Fatal injury rates in 1992/93 continued to fall in construction and manufacturing.

13   Considered by industrial sector, the 1992/93 final fatal rates are expected to be lower in construction and manufacturing and substantially lower in the energy sector. From a longer term perspective, the fatal injury rate has fallen steadily over the last five years in construction and is now about half the level seen throughout the 1960s and 1970s. In manufacturing, the fatal injury rate has fallen from around three deaths per 100 000 in most years in the 1960s and 1970s to around two in the late 1980s and has dropped again in each of the last two years, with an expected rate of 1.4 in 1992/93 on finalisation. In energy, the rate has fluctuated around 6.5 per 100 000 employees (excluding the fatalities in the Piper Alpha disaster). The rate in agriculture in 1992/93 is likely to be more in line with that seen in the previous six years, compared with the lower rate in 1991/92.

14   There was a reduction in 1992/93 in the provisional number of deaths of employees caused by a fall from a height, 56 compared with 83 in 1991/92, a proportional decrease twice as great as that in the overall reduction of the number of deaths. Fatal injuries caused by contact with electricity returned to the level occurring in the late 1980s after a sharp reduction in 1991/92.

15   Where the nature of injury was identified over one fifth were contusions including crushing injuries. Nearly two fifths of fatalities were caused by multiple injuries or an unknown nature of injury. The reduction in the number and proportion of fatalities caused by fractures noted in 1991/92 continued in 1992/93.

16   All but eight of the 227 fatalities reported so far to HSE's Field Operations Division and the local authorities were male. There was a slight rise in the number of young people (aged 16-19) killed at work in 1992/93 compared with the previous year, but this was still approximately half the number fatally injured in the late 1980s.

The non-fatal major injury rate continued to fall in 1992/93 although it is expected to be only marginally lower than in 1991/92.

17   The ***non-fatal major*** injury rate for employees fell slightly to an estimated final rate of 81 per 100 000 employees in 1992/93 with a substantial drop in the rate in the construction industry and a rise in agriculture to the highest level since RIDDOR was introduced in 1986. In services, the rate on finalisation is expected to be on the same level as the average for the past six years.

The over-3-day injury rate has fallen each year since 1986/87 and is expected to be slightly lower still in 1992/93.

18   The ***over-3-day*** injury rate also fell, the estimated final rate is around 680 per 100 000 employees. The continued reduction from 760 per 100 000 employees in 1986/87 is wholly attributable to the changes in patterns in employment. There were falls in the rates in the energy and construction sectors, little change in manufacturing and services, but a rise in the rate in the agricultural sector.

Self-employed people

19   The provisional 1992/93 figure of 60 reported fatalities to self-employed people is expected to reach about 67 when finalised. Over 70% of the deaths reported so far were in the

agricultural and construction sectors, although these areas account for only about three in ten self-employed workers.

20   The estimated final fatal injury rate for the self-employed is 2.2 per 100 000 workers, a marginal reduction from the rate in 1991/92, but maintaining the slight downward trend seen since 1989/90.

21   In contrast to the previous five years, the fatal injury rate for the self-employed in agriculture looks likely to be below that for employees. This is due both to a substantial reduction in the expected number of fatalities among the self-employed and to an increase in the estimated number of self-employed people in the agricultural sector. However this should be looked at against a background of relatively small numbers of both accidents and workers (the latter being estimated from the Labour Force Survey), so small changes can lead to marked fluctuations in the rate.

Figure 4   Fatal injuries to self-employed. Injury incidence rates 1981 to 1992/93p

Injury rate (per 100 000 workers)

Notes
p   provisional

Numbers in brackets are the deaths in each of the years

Expected increase from provisional to final

1981	1982	1983	1984	1985	86/87	87/88	88/89	89/90	90/91	91/92	92/93p
2.6	2.3	3.0	2.5	2.8	2.0	3.0	2.7	3.3	2.7	2.3	2.2/1.9
(54)	(48)	(65)	(60)	(71)	(52)	(84)	(80)	(105)	(87)	(71)	(60)

Members of the public

There was an increase in the fatal injuries to members of the public in 1992/93 compared with the unusually low number in 1991/92; most of these fatalities continued to be in the service sector.

22   The provisional 1992/93 figure for fatal injuries to members of the public caused by work activity was 121 and with the upward revision expected on finalisation is likely to be one of the highest figures since 1986/87. Most of these injuries occurred in the service sector. The reduction in the number of fatal injuries in the agricultural sector to members of the public seen in 1991/92 was not sustained.

23   As well as fatalities, major injuries to members of the public are reportable. The number of reports fell each year from 1986/87 to 1990/91, rose in 1991/92, but looks likely to be lower in 1992/93 than in the previous year.

OCCUPATIONAL ILL HEALTH

Data sources

24   The principal data source is the counts of new cases of industrial disease recorded under the *Industrial Injuries (II) Scheme* which has the advantage of providing data on individually examined and validated cases. However it is affected from time to time by changes in the rules determining entitlement to benefit, and by factors affecting uptake of the benefit, but provides a reliable indicator of the absolute lower limit of the number of more serious cases of industrial disease. Some areas of ill health in the workplace are not covered by the II Scheme and are seriously under-counted. A summary of diseases covered and numbers of cases reported under the Scheme in the latest year available is given in Table 5, along with parallel estimates from other sources, including *RIDDOR* ill-health reports, where these are available.

25   Two important supplementary sources of data have been developed in recent years. Surveillance schemes to monitor occupational respiratory disease (*SWORD*) and skin disease (*EPIDERM*) provide information on cases referred to specialists and identified by them as probably occupational. The supplementary trailer questionnaire to the 1990 *Labour Force Survey (LFS)* has also provided an insight into the scale and distribution of some work-related illnesses, based on respondents' own perception of the link between their occupation and ill health.

Disease by occupation from the Labour Force Survey

Two broad patterns of disease risk can be distinguished for manual and non-manual occupations

26   Some interesting if predictable observations can be made from the data collected from the Labour Force Survey. Risk of disease proved to be highest in coal mining - although a nearly 12-fold excess risk for cases 'caused' by this work must be treated with caution due to the difficulty of defining the size of the workforce in this rapidly contracting industry.

27   Higher risks of disease, eg musculo-skeletal conditions, lower respiratory disease, deafness, and the long-term effects of injury are also found in other manual occupations. The construction industry, with a two-fold raised risk for all ill health 'caused' by work, was noted for back problems and was also responsible for high rates of skin disease in men. Employment in metal and electrical processing, also approaching double the risk for ill health 'caused' by work, is associated with high rates of deafness and Vibration White Finger, while asthma and eye problems are found with work in other materials processing, and Repetitive Strain Injury (RSI) where workers are engaged in repetitive assembly, inspection and packing. Musculo-skeletal conditions and the after-effects of trauma affect men and women employed in transport and materials handling. Painters, and farmers, fishermen and forestry workers have patterns of disease typically associated with manual employment, although with low rates of occupational deafness reported among the latter group.

28   The pattern of disease reported for the non-manual occupations is rather different. Nurses reported particularly high rates for back problems and were at higher risk of work-related infections than other non-manual workers. This was also the case for those employed in education and welfare. Stress/depression was the main cause of work-related illness among teachers. Skin diseases and deafness were noted in those employed in science and engineering, and varicose veins among saleswomen (otherwise the healthiest group identified). For office-based workers (professional and clerical), stress/depression, headache

and eyestrain and musculo-skeletal disorders were most commonly reported. Workers in catering, cleaning and hairdressing suffered significantly higher risk of skin disease, plus the more common musculo-skeletal problems. Police and others in security suffered from the effects of trauma; members of the armed forces reported the effects of trauma and deafness.

Work-related ill health is more common in men than in women, particularly for those over retirement age.

29   More men than women in all age groups reported a work-related illness, although there was a clear trend in the male/female ratio across age groups, so that while three times as many men as women over retirement age reported a work-related illness, the same was true for only a third more men than women in the 16-44 age group.

Asbestos-related disease

The numbers of new cases of mesothelioma and asbestosis continue to rise.

30   The growth in the number of new cases of ***mesothelioma*** continues; of particular concern is the increase among younger age groups. Over 1000 deaths were recorded for mesothelioma in 1991, a 15% rise on the 1990 total. Preliminary analysis of all deaths with a mention of mesothelioma on the death certificate has suggested that the incidence in successive birth cohorts also appears to be increasing.

31   The number of new cases of ***asbestosis*** diagnosed by the II Special Medical Boards in the last two years for those first exposed in the 1960s (as reported by the patient to the examining doctor at the time of diagnosis) nearly doubled between 1990 and 1991 (see Figure 5). There is also some evidence of cases arising from exposure after the introduction of the 1969 Regulations.

Figure 5   Asbestosis. Cases newly diagnosed.

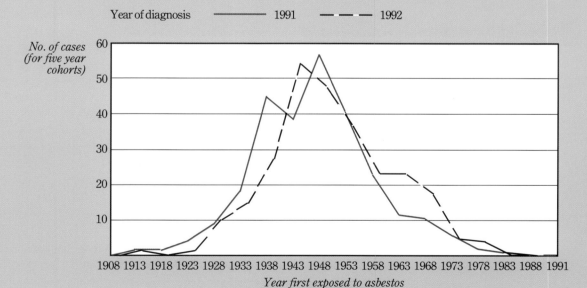

Cases for which a year of first exposure was not reported have been excluded

32   The estimated total number of deaths due to asbestos (mesothelioma, lung cancer and asbestosis) is now approaching 3000 annually (estimated at 2850 in 1991).

Other recent trends in occupational health statistics

Reported cases of occupational asthma and musculo-skeletal problems are rising, but new cases of occupational deafness and Vibration White Finger fell in 1991/92.

33   Figures for ***pneumoconiosis*** (other than asbestosis) have remained steady, fluctuating around an average of about 400 cases per year since 1984, with no indication of a resumption of the previous downward trend.

34   The number of new cases qualifying for disablement benefit for ***occupational deafness*** has gradually declined to 972 cases in 1991/92. Reported cases of ***Vibration White Finger*** (a prescribed disease since 1985), often found in association with occupational deafness in the workplace, reached a peak of 5401 cases in 1990/91, but have fallen for 1991/92 back to former levels.

35   Numbers assessed under the II Scheme for ***occupational asthma*** have continued to grow since prescription of this disease in 1982, both for the sensitising agents originally prescribed and also as new categories of agent have been added, in 1986 and again in September 1991, when an 'open category' was added. Comparison with the SWORD data shows that not all cases are being picked up. Improvements in reporting are likely to explain the doubling of the notifications of asthma under the SWORD scheme to over 1000 in 1992, nearly double the number of cases recorded under the II Scheme in that year but still considered to underestimate the true number of annual cases (which may be up to one and a half times higher).

36   Cases of ***musculo-skeletal problems*** (for the narrow range of conditions recorded under the Scheme: tenosynovitis, upper limb cramp and beat conditions) are rising but a potentially very large pool of non-compensatable cases remains unmonitored, as indicated by the LFS.

37   ***Dermatitis*** is also poorly enumerated by the count of assessed disablements. Somewhere between 3000 and 5000 new cases caused or made worse by work are serious enough to be seen by consultant dermatologists under the EPIDERM scheme. A far greater number - estimated at over 60 000 - were seen by GPs in 1989, a number not out of line with the prevalence estimate (of 85 000) from the LFS of skin disease.

38   Numbers working in the ***lead industry*** and therefore monitored for exposure to lead in the workplace continue to decline. The proportions of workers with blood lead levels in the higher concentration bands show a steady decline.

SOURCES AND DEFINITIONS   **Fatal, major and over-3-day injuries**   *Tables 1 to 4*

39   The source of these tables is reports to enforcing authorities made under the Notification of Accidents and Dangerous Occurrences Regulations 1980 (NADOR) for the years 1981 to 1985 and the Reporting of Injuries, Diseases and Dangerous Occurrences Regulations 1985 (RIDDOR) from 1986/87 onwards, when the publication of the statistics was changed to a financial year basis. The number of reports received in 1992/93 is shown in Table B.

90

Table B   Injury reports received by HSE enforcing authorities, 1992/93p

Field Operations Division	139260
Mines	2158
Explosives	89
Railway	4218
Offshore Safety Division	588
Local authorities	22500
All enforcement authorities	168813

p provisional

40   RIDDOR also extended the definition of notifiable major injuries as defined in regulations 3(1) and 3(2). This means that in Table 3 the RIDDOR data are not comparable with NADOR based data presented in previous publications but should be looked at separately to determine general trends. RIDDOR also reinstated the employer's duty to report injuries resulting in an absence from normal work of more than three days. This series of data is shown in Table 4.

41   Fatal and major injuries are reportable for employees (including trainees), self-employed people and also members of the public if they are judged to have arisen from work activity. The definition of a fatal injury includes a death occurring up to a year after the accident. Major injuries include nearly all fractures, amputations, loss of sight of an eye and injuries resulting in the person being admitted immediately into hospital for more than 24 hours. A full definition can be found in the Statistical Supplement to this report.

42   Injuries causing an absence from work of over 3 days are also reportable for employees and the self-employed but not for members of the public.

43   The injury data are classified by industry group using the 1980 Standard Industrial Classification. Injury rates are calculated using estimates of employment provided by the Employment Department. In this report the estimates are based on the 1991 Census of Employment updated by Employment Department using monthly and quarterly surveys of employers and the Labour Force Survey.

ENQUIRIES   44   Enquiries about statistics for injuries arising from work activity, dangerous occurrences, enforcement action and gas safety should be addressed to:

Statistical Services Unit
Health and Safety Executive
Room 512, Daniel House
Trinity Road
Bootle, Merseyside L20 7HE
Telephone: 051-951-4604/4842

45   Enquiries about occupational ill-health statistics should be addressed to:

Epidemiology and Medical Statistics Unit
Health and Safety Executive
Room 244, Magdalen House
Bootle, Merseyside L20 3QZ
Telephone: 051-951-4540/4542

Table 1 Injuries by industry and severity of injury 1992/93p
As reported to all enforcement authorities

Standard Industrial Classification (SIC 80)		Fatal injuries	Non-fatal major injuries	Fatal and major injuries: rate per 100 000 employees	Over-3-day injuries	All reported injuries Number	All reported injuries Rate per 100 000
Agriculture, forestry and fishing (a)	0	18	414	169.4	1398	1830	717.6
Agriculture and horticulture	01	16	384	166.3	1247	1647	684.5
Forestry	02	2	24	337.6	130	156	2026.0
Fishing (a)	03	–	6	n/a	21	27	n/a
Energy and water supply industries (b)	1	19	745	198.9	6215	6979	1816.5
Coal extraction and manufacture of solid fuels:	11	8	371	662.6	1871	2250	3933.6
of which: Coal mines	1113	7	332	650.7	1723	2062	3957.8
Open cast coal workings	1114	1	37	904.8	136	174	4142.9
Coke ovens	12	–	2	285.7	37	39	5571.4
Extraction of mineral oil and natural gas (b)	13	4	77	162.0	517	598	1196.0
Mineral oil processing	14	–	17	100.0	98	115	676.5
Nuclear fuel production	15	–	15	99.3	136	151	1000.0
Production and distribution of electricity, gas and other forms of energy	16	7	199	106.2	2768	2974	1533.8
Water supply industry	17	–	64	127.2	788	852	1693.8
Extraction of minerals and ores other than fuels; manufacture of metals, mineral products and chemicals	2	22	1012	171.1	8416	9450	1563.3
Extraction and preparation of metalliferous ores and extraction of minerals not elsewhere specified	21/23	7	101	435.5	583	691	2786.3
Metal manufacturing	22	–	276	219.6	2230	2506	1993.6
Manufacture of non-metallic mineral products	24	7	282	186.1	2555	2844	1831.3
Chemical industry	25	8	341	119.0	2979	3328	1134.3
Production of man-made fibres	26	–	12	222.2	69	81	1500.0
Metal goods, engineering and vehicles industries	3	23	1878	99.7	16 166	18 067	947.4
Manufacture of metal goods not elsewhere specified	31	6	489	192.2	3657	4152	1611.8
Mechanical engineering	32	11	545	88.5	4317	4873	775.3
Manufacture of office machinery and data processing equipment	33	–	34	51.6	180	214	324.7
Electrical and electronic engineering	34	2	284	62.0	2443	2729	591.7
Manufacture of motor vehicles and parts thereof	35	2	264	118.5	3186	3452	1538.3
Manufacture of other transport equipment	36	2	234	127.9	2095	2331	1263.4
Instrument engineering	37	–	28	32.9	288	316	371.3
Other manufacturing industries	4	13	2393	135.9	22727	25133	1419.2
Food, drink and tobacco manufacturing industries	41/42	7	1052	219.7	12278	13337	2767.0
Textile industries	43	–	178	105.7	1411	1589	943.6
Manufacture of leather or leather goods	44	–	10	64.1	121	131	839.7
Footwear and clothing industries	45	–	80	37.5	670	750	351.9
Timber and wooden furniture industries	46	2	370	200.8	1995	2367	1277.4
Manufacture of paper and paper products, printing and publishing	47	2	347	77.6	3088	3437	764.0
Processing of rubber and plastics	48	2	319	168.2	2840	3161	1655.8

Notes
(a) Excludes sea fishing. (b) Includes the number of injuries in the oil and gas industry collected under offshore installations safety legislation.

Fatal injuries	Non-fatal major injuries	Over-3-day injuries	All reported injuries	Fatal injuries	Non-fatal major injuries	Fatal injuries	Non-fatal major injuries	Over-3-day injuries	All reported injuries
19	105	123	247	12	48	49	567	1521	2137
14	81	91	186	12	45	42	510	1338	1890
4	23	32	59	–	2	6	49	162	217
1	1	–	2	–	1	1	8	21	30
1	11	25	37	2	26	22	782	6240	7044
1	8	23	32	–	4	9	383	1894	2286
1	5	23	29	–	2	8	339	1746	2093
–	3	–	3	–	1	1	41	136	178
–	–	–	–	–	–	–	2	37	39
–	–	–	–	–	–	4	77	517	598
–	–	–		–	–	–	17	98	115
–	1	–	1	–	1	–	17	136	153
–	–	1	1	1	16	8	215	2769	2992
–	2	1	3	1	5	1	71	789	861
–	35	46	81	–	12	22	1059	8462	9543
–	8	11	19	–	2	7	111	594	712
–	5	4	9	–	–	–	281	2234	2515
–	12	16	28	–	4	7	298	2571	2876
–	10	14	24	–	6	8	357	2993	3358
–	–	1	1	–	–	–	12	70	82
1	44	51	96	–	18	24	1940	16217	18 181
–	16	11	27	–	1	6	506	3668	4180
1	11	28	40	–	11	12	567	4345	4924
–	–	1	1	–	2	–	36	181	217
–	10	8	18	–	–	2	294	2451	2747
–	5	1	6	–	–	2	269	3187	3458
–	2	2	4	–	3	2	239	2097	2338
–	–	–	–	–	1	–	29	288	317
1	48	76	125	–	19	14	2460	22803	25277
–	14	30	44	–	4	7	1070	12308	13385
–	–	–	–	–	–	–	178	1411	1589
–	–	–	–	–	–	–	10	121	131
–	2	1	3	–	–	–	82	671	753
1	20	29	50	–	6	3	396	2024	2423
–	5	5	10	–	2	2	354	3093	3449
–	6	8	14	–	2	2	327	2848	3177

juries arising from shore based services only. Excludes incidents
ed under merchant shipping legislation.
not available   p   provisional

93

Table 1 (cont'd)

		Employees (including trainees)				
	Fatal injuries	Non-fatal major injuries	Fatal and major injuries: rate per 100000 employees	Over-3-day injuries	All reported injur	
					Number	Rate 100
Other manufacturing industries 49	–	37	56.2	324	361	548
Total manufacturing industries 2-4	58	5283	124.7	47309	52650	1229
Construction 5	63	2062	246.8	11675	13800	1602
Distribution, hotels and catering; repairs 6	15	2093	47.0	15159	17267	384
Wholesale distribution (including dealing in scrap and waste materials) 61/62	9	388	46.5	2170	2637	300
Commission agents 63	–	1	3.0	11	12	35
Retail distribution 64/65	–	899	39.8	8265	9164	405
Hotels and catering 66	3	418	36.1	2204	2625	225
Repair of consumer goods and vehicles 67	3	387	221.5	2509	2899	1646
Transport and communication (c) 7	39	1311	106.3	15531	16881	1329
Railways 71	11	326	251.7	3883	4220	3151
Other inland transport 72	15	327	87.1	3145	3487	888
Sea transport (c) 74	4	4	25.8	27	35	112
Air transport 75	2	41	64.8	423	466	701
Supporting services to transport 76	4	117	165.8	993	1114	1526
Miscellaneous transport services and storage not elsewhere specified 77	2	101	53.7	935	1038	541
Postal services and telecommunications 79	1	395	103.8	6125	6521	1709
Banking, finance, insurance, business services and leasing 8	6	266	10.6	1501	1773	69
Banking and finance 81	–	63	10.9	381	444	76
Insurance, except for compulsory social security 82	–	16	6.3	131	147	58
Business services 83	2	113	7.9	619	734	50
Renting of moveables 84	4	61	56.0	196	261	225
Owning and dealing in real estate 85	–	13	7.9	174	187	113
Other services 9	31	4056	59.6	37753	41840	609
Public administration, national defence, compulsory social security and sanitary services 91/92	23	1496	83.9	18118	19637	1088
Education 93	1	1164	64.2	4858	6023	333
Research and development 94	–	65	75.1	335	400	462
Medical and other health services, veterinary services 95	1	752	48.4	10046	10799	693
Other services provided to general public 96	–	267	29.3	2629	2896	317
Recreational services and other cultural services 97	5	274	56.6	1403	1682	341
Personal services 98	1	38	20.5	364	403	217
Domestic services 99	–	–	–	–	–	
Total service industries 6-9	91	7726	51.5	69944	77761	511
Unclassified	–	296	n/a	1726	2022	n
All industries	249	16526	80.0	138267	155042	739

Notes
(a) Excludes sea fishing.   (b) Includes the number of injuries in the oil and gas industry collected under offshore installations safety legislation.

94

Self-employed				Members of the public		Total			
Fatal injuries	Non-fatal major injuries	Over-3-day injuries	All reported injuries	Fatal injuries	Non-fatal major injuries	Fatal injuries	Non-fatal major injuries	Over-3-day injuries	All reported injuries
–	1	3	4	–	5	–	43	327	370
2	127	173	302	–	49	60	5459	47482	53001
24	678	1278	1980	5	100	92	2840	12953	15885
6	24	44	74	13	1299	34	3416	15203	18653
2	10	13	25	1	15	12	413	2183	2608
–	–	–	–	–	–	–	1	11	12
1	5	10	16	3	808	4	1712	8275	9991
–	3	7	10	9	471	12	892	2211	3115
3	6	14	23	–	5	6	398	2523	2927
2	13	12	27	3	34	44	1358	15543	16945
–	—	—	—	—	—	11	326	3883	4220
2	5	5	12	1	5	18	337	3150	3505
–	—	–	–	–	–	4	4	27	35
–	1	1	2	–	3	2	45	424	471
–	3	4	7	2	20	6	140	997	1143
–	–	1	1	–	–	2	101	936	1039
–	4	1	5	–	6	1	405	6126	6532
–	8	13	21	3	82	9	356	1514	1879
–	1	3	4	–	16	–	80	384	464
–	–	1	1	–	–	–	16	132	148
–	2	6	8	3	56	5	171	625	801
–	5	3	8	–	2	4	68	199	271
–	–	–	–	–	8	–	21	174	195
6	83	384	473	83	8663	120	12802	38137	51059
3	43	321	367	16	666	42	2205	18439	20686
–	7	11	18	3	4788	4	5959	4869	10832
–	–	3	3	–	1	n/a	66	338	404
–	4	6	10	21	895	22	1651	10052	11725
–	2	4	6	31	1067	31	1336	2633	4000
2	27	38	67	12	1243	19	1544	1441	3004
–	–	1	1	–	3	1	41	365	407
1	–	–	1	–	–	1	–	–	1
14	128	453	595	102	10078	207	17932	70397	88536
–	41	46	87	–	101	–	438	1772	2210
50	1090	2098	3248	121	10402	430	28018	140365	168813

njuries arising from shore based services only. Excludes incidents
rted under merchant shipping legislation.
not available   p   provisional

Table 2 Fatal injuries reported to enforcement authorities by industry 1981 - 1992/93p

Standard Industrial Classification(1980)	Agriculture forestry and fishing (b)	Energy and water supply industries (c) (d) (e)	Total manu-facturing industries (d)	Construction	Service industries (f)	Unclassified	All industries
Division Year (a)	0	1	2-4	5	6-9		
Employment status							
Injury numbers 1981	31	54	123	105	102	26	441
1982	27	77	137	100	117	14	472
1983	29	48	118	118	111	24	448
1984	29	48	142	100	105	14	438
1985	20	46	124	104	99	7	400
Employees 1986/87	27	30	109	99	80	10	355
1987/88	21	33	99	103	96	9	361
1988/89	21	203 (g)	94	101	109	1	529 (g)
1989/90	23	31	108	100	108	–	370
1990/91	25	27	88	96	110	–	346
1991/92	18	31	68	83	97	–	297
1992/93p	18	19	58	63	91	–	249
1981	26	–	6	11	10	1	54
1982	22	–	2	18	6	–	48
1983	26	1	9	22	7	–	65
1984	25	–	5	17	13	–	60
Self-employed 1985	44	–	–	22	5	–	71
1986/87	17	–	1	26	8	–	52
1987/88	31	–	5	40	8	–	84
1988/89	25	2	7	36	10	–	80
1989/90	30	–	7	54	14	–	105
1990/91	27	–	10	28	22	–	87
1991/92	32	1	8	16	14	–	71
1992/93p	19	1	2	24	14	–	60
1981	13	3	5	12	38	–	71
1982	17	1	5	13	47	–	83
1983	9	6	7	11	52	–	85
1984	7	23	3	7	61	4	105
1985	11	17	5	13	110 (h)	3	159 (h)
Members of the public 1986/87	16	7	5	14	43	7	92
1987/88	10	2	–	15	82	4	113
1988/89	15	2	4	14	84	2	121
1989/90	12	4	3	11	176(i)	–	206(i)
1990/91	15	3	4	9	108	–	139
1991/92	5	2	2	6	90	–	105
1992/93p	12	2	–	5	102	–	121

Standard Industrial Classification(1980)	Agriculture forestry and fishing (b)	Energy and water supply industries (c) (d) (e)	Total manu- facturing industries (d)	Construction	Service industries (f)	Unclassified	All industries
Division Year (a)	0	1	2-4	5	6-9		
Incidence rates (per 100 000)							
1981	8.8	7.8	2.0	9.7	0.8	n/a	2.1
1982	7.8	11.5	2.4	9.7	0.9	n/a	2.3
1983	8.6	7.5	2.2	11.6	0.8	n/a	2.2
1984	8.8	7.9	2.7	9.8	0.8	n/a	2.1
1985	6.1	8.0	2.4	10.5	0.7	n/a	1.9
1986/87	8.6	5.8	2.1	10.2	0.6	n/a	1.7
1987/88	6.8	6.7	1.9	10.3	0.7	n/a	1.7
Employees 1988/89	7.0	42.7(g)	1.8	9.9	0.7	n/a	2.4(g)
1989/90	8.1	6.9	2.1	9.4	0.7	n/a	1.7
1990/91	9.0	6.1	1.8	9.3	0.7	n/a	1.6
1991/92	6.7	7.4	1.5	8.8	0.6	n/a	1.4
1992/93p	7.1	4.9	1.4	7.3	0.6	n/a	1.2
1981	10.4	n/a	4.1	2.8	0.8	n/a	2.6
1982	8.9	n/a	1.4	4.5	0.5	n/a	2.3
1983	10.6	n/a	6.0	5.4	0.5	n/a	3.0
1984	10.0	n/a	2.8	3.7	0.8	n/a	2.5
1985	17.7	n/a	–	4.7	0.3	n/a	2.8
1986/87	6.9	n/a	0.5	5.3	0.5	n/a	2.0
1987/88	12.7	n/a	2.0	7.4	0.5	n/a	3.0
Self-employed 1988/89	10.3	n/a	2.7	6.1	0.5	n/a	2.7
1989/90	12.3	n/a	2.5	7.5	0.7	n/a	3.3
1990/91	10.9	n/a	3.7	3.9	1.1	n/a	2.7
1991/92	13.0	n/a	2.8	2.5	0.7	n/a	2.3
1992/93p	6.9	n/a	0.6	3.7	0.8	n/a	1.9

Notes

(a) 1981-85 calendar years - reported under the Notification of Accidents and Dangerous Occurrences Regulations (NADOR) 1980. 1986/87 onwards years commencing 1 April - reported under the Reporting of Injuries, Diseases and Dangerous Occurrences Regulations (RIDDOR) 1985.

(b) Excludes sea fishing.

(c) Includes the number of injuries in the offshore oil and gas industry collected under offshore safety legislation.

(d) Fatal injuries to the self-employed and members of the public reported to the Mines and Quarries Inspectorate for the years 1981 to 1984 are included with injuries reported to employees.

(e) Due to the small number of self-employed workers in this sector, the calculation of injury incidence rates would not be reliable.

(f) Fatal injuries to the self-employed reported to local authorities for the years 1981-1985 are included with injuries reported to employees.

(g) Data includes the 167 fatalities of the Piper Alpha disaster, 6 July 1988.

(h) Data includes the 56 fatalities to members of the public in the Bradford City Football Club fire disaster.

(i) Data includes the 95 fatalities to members of the public in the Hillsborough disaster, 15 April 1989.

p provisional

n/a not available

Table 3 Non-fatal major injuries reported to enforcement authorities by industry 1986/87 - 1992/93p

Employment status	Standard Industrial Classification(1980) Division Year	Agriculture forestry and fishing (b) 0	Energy and water supply industries (c) (d) (e) 1	Total manu-facturing industries (d) 2-4	Construction 5	Service industries (f) 6-9	Unclassified	All industries
Injury numbers	1986/87	429	1718	7378	2736	8057	377	20 695
	1987/88	498	1397	7233	2767	7936	226	20 057
	1988/89	451	1262	7380	2907	7810	134	19 994
Employees	1989/90	403	1140	7365	3180	8189	119	20 396
	1990/91	443	1061	6794	2907	8514	177	19 896
	1991/92	404	935	5827	2570	7640	221	17 597
	1992/93p	414	745	5283	2062	7726	296	16 526
	1986/87	72	5	89	443	80	1	690
	1987/88	91	6	100	561	105	4	867
	1988/89	132	5	134	753	124	4	1152
Self-employed	1989/90	102	6	132	927	138	5	1310
	1990/91	115	13	129	931	119	19	1326
	1991/92	77	11	131	729	125	28	1101
	1992/93p	105	11	127	678	128	41	1090
	1986/87	58	30	65	162	14 214	46	14 575
	1987/88	59	17	57	153	12 390	204	12 880
	1988/89	89	29	57	132	12 123	184	12 614
Members of the public	1989/90	65	16	24	113	11 119	41	11 378
	1990/91	50	22	39	123	9699	48	9981
	1991/92	54	12	34	148	10 705	56	11 009
	1992/93p	48	26	49	100	10 078	101	10 402
Incidence rates (per 100 000)	1986/87	136.5	330.3	145.0	282.7	57.5	n/a	99.1
	1987/88	162.0	281.9	142.0	276.5	54.9	n/a	94.0
	1988/89	151.3	265.6	143.7	285.9	52.5	n/a	91.4
Employees	1989/90	141.9	253.2	144.4	298.8	53.4	n/a	91.8
	1990/91	160.3	239.9	136.1	281.5	55.3	n/a	89.9
	1991/92	150.0	223.2	128.8	272.4	49.7	n/a	81.7
	1992/93p	162.4	193.9	123.5	239.5	50.9	n/a	78.8
	1986/87	29.0	n/a	42.6	91.0	4.9	n/a	26.9
	1987/88	37.1	n/a	40.7	103.5	5.9	n/a	31.0
	1988/89	54.3	n/a	52.1	127.0	6.8	n/a	39.4
Self-employed	1989/90	42.0	n/a	47.1	128.4	7.1	n/a	41.2
	1990/91	46.6	n/a	47.6	129.7	6.0	n/a	41.2
	1991/92	31.2	n/a	45.2	112.5	6.7	n/a	35.9
	1992/93p	38.2	n/a	36.9	104.8	7.1	n/a	35.3

Table 4 Over-3-day injuries reported to enforcement authorities analysed by industry 1986/87 - 1992/93p

Standard Industrial Classification(1980)		Agriculture forestry and fishing (b)	Energy and water supply industries (c) (d) (e)	Total manu-facturing industries (d)	Construction	Service industries (f)	Unclassified	All industries
Employment status	Division Year	0	1	2-4	5	6-9		
Injury numbers	1986/87	1043	19 621 (d)	54 046 (d)	16 468	65 958	1875	159 011
	1987/88	1349	15 798	52 734	16 622	69 085	4264	159 852
	1988/89	1473	13 728	56 141	16 597	71 268	3912	163 119
Employees	1989/90	1496	11 684	60 006	17 177	74 405	476	165 244
	1990/91	1318	10 256	56 403	16 689	75 344	801	160 811
	1991/92	1423	8232	52 420	14 989	74 219	1223	152 506
	1992/93p	1398	6215	47 309	11 675	69 944	1726	138 267
	1986/87	108	8	99	704	104	6	1029
	1987/88	117	10	122	763	156	1	1159
	1988/89	142	10	128	969	245	9	1503
Self-employed	1989/90	130	21	148	1310	251	5	1865
	1990/91	104	20	146	1554	226	27	2077
	1991/92	118	43	160	1231	232	48	1832
	1992/93p	123	25	173	1278	453	46	2098
Incidence rates (per 100 000)	1986/87	331.7	3771.8	1061.9	1701.8	471.1	n/a	761.1
	1987/88	438.7	3188.3	1035.5	1660.9	478.1	n/a	748.9
Employees	1988/89	494.1	2889.5	1093.1	1632.3	478.6	n/a	747.7
	1989/90	526.8	2595.3	1176.5	1614.2	485.4	n/a	743.4
	1990/91	477.0	2318.8	1130.3	1616.2	489.5	n/a	726.5
	1991/92	528.2	1965.1	1158.3	1588.7	482.9	n/a	708.5
	1992/93p	548.2	1617.6	1104.7	1356.0	460.7	n/a	659.5
	1986/87	43.5	n/a	47.4	144.6	6.4	n/a	40.1
	1987/88	47.8	n/a	45.5	140.8	8.8	n/a	41.4
	1988/89	58.4	n/a	49.8	163.4	13.4	n/a	51.4
Self-employed	1989/90	53.3	n/a	52.9	181.4	13.0	n/a	58.6
	1990/91	42.1	n/a	53.9	216.4	11.4	n/a	64.5
	1991/92	47.8	n/a	55.2	190.0	12.4	n/a	59.8
	1992/93p	44.8	n/a	50.3	197.5	25.0	n/a	67.9

Notes (for Tables 3 and 4)
(a)   Excludes sea fishing.
(b)   Includes the number of injuries in the offshore oil and gas industry collected under offshore safety legislation.
(c)   Due to the small number of self-employed workers in this sector, the calculation of injury incidence rates would not be reliable.
(d)   Excludes over-3-day injuries reported to the Mines and Quarries Inspectorate for non-British coal mines and for other mining and quarrying activities: figures not readily available.
p   provisional
n/a   not available

Table 5 Cases of occupational disease reported from surveillance schemes and other sources 1992

Scheme	DSS II (1)p	RIDDOR (2)p	SWORD (estimated)	Death certificates (3)(1991)	Estimated prevalence LFS (4)('000s)
	——— Annual incidence 1992 ———				
Lung diseases					
Prescribed:					
Pneumoconiosis (excluding asbestosis)	411	3	418	287	13.2
Asbestosis	354	7	-	106 (7)	6.3
Byssinosis	4	0	4	16	-
Farmer's lung, allergic alveolitis	5	6	97	8	-
Occupational asthma	553	63	1047	-	19.7
Mesothelioma	551	7	723	1017	-
Lung cancer (asbestos)	54	0	146	57 (8)	-
Lung cancer (other prescribed agents)	6	0	-	-	-
Bilateral pleural thickening	160	-	-	-	-
Other prescribed lung diseases	5	-	-	-	-
Other SWORD cases:					
Benign pleural disease	-	-	681	-	-
Bronchitis	-	-	133	-	34.9
Building-related illness	-	-	11	-	2.5 (9)
Infectious diseases	-	-	53	-	-
Inhalation accidents	-	-	251	-	-
Other SWORD	-	-	71	-	-
LFS groupings:					
Other lower respiratory disease	-	-	-	-	26.2
Total lung diseases	**2103**	**86**	**3635**	**1491**	**102.8**

Notes
(1) Industrial Injuries Scheme administered by the DSS, new cases of assessed disablement seen by Special Medical Boards
(2) Year ending 31 March 1993
(3) For mesothelioma and asbestosis, death certificates with a mention of mesothelioma or asbestosis anywhere on the death certificate are counted. For other diseases, numbers with the disease specified as underlying cause of death only are counted
(4) Prevalence estimates for self-reported conditions considered to be caused by work, England and Wales 1990
(5) Year to 30 September 1992
(6) Year to 31 December 1992
(7) Excludes asbestosis in conjunction with mesothelioma or lung cancer
(8) Lung cancer with asbestosis
(9) Described as 'Sick Building Syndrome' type symptoms. classified under headache and eyestrain
(10) Chrome ulcer, folliculitis and acne only
(11) Annual estimate based on reports from 50% of UK consultants in the first three months of the project
p   provisional

Scheme	Annual incidence 1992			Estimated prevalence LFS (4)('000s)
	DSS II (5)p	RIDDOR (2)p	EPIDERM (1993)	
Other diseases				
Prescribed:				
Occupational deafness (6)	972	-	-	103.1
Dermatitis	411	2 (10)	2636 (11)	54.2
Tenosynovitis	649	-	-	21.1
Vibration White Finger	2369	97	-	7.3
Cramp of hand or forearm	52	-	-	-
Beat conditions	317	-	-	-
Viral hepatitis	4	15	-	2.4
Tuberculosis	3	12	-	1.9
Leptospirosis	1	10	-	-
Other infections	4	17	-	23.4
Poisonings	8	5	-	5.4
Occupation cancers	23	4	-	-
Other prescribed conditions	91	24	-	-
Other RIDDOR conditions	-	3	-	-
LFS groupings:				
Stress/depression	-	-	-	104.9
Headache and 'eyestrain' excluding Sick Building Syndrome symptoms (9)	-	-	-	43.4
Heart disease	-	-	-	45.0
Varicose veins	-	-	-	3.0
Upper respiratory disease	-	-	-	20.3
RSI excluding tenosynovitis	-	-	-	28.5
Musculo-skeletal conditions excluding RSI	-	-	-	543.2
Trauma (long term sequalae)	-	-	-	102.3
Eye conditions	-	-	-	22.4
Exhaustion, ME, symptoms	-	-	-	13.1
Other diseases excluding neoplasms	-	-	-	51.5
Total other diseases	**4904**	**189**	**-**	**1196.4**

ANNEXES

Annex 1 **FUNCTIONS OF THE HEALTH AND SAFETY COMMISSION AND EXECUTIVE AND ADVISORY COMMITTEES**

FUNCTIONS The Health and Safety Commission and Health and Safety Executive are bodies created by the Health and Safety at Work etc Act 1974 ('the 1974 Act'). The Act lays the responsibility for industrial safety and health upon employers and employees. The Commission and Executive act as prime movers, acting in accord with industry and setting and refining a framework for action by others.

The Commission is responsible to the Secretary of State for Employment and to other Secretaries of State for the administration of the Act. Its duties are to take appropriate steps to secure the health, safety and welfare of persons at work; to protect the public against risks to health and safety arising out of work activities and to control the keeping and use of explosives, highly flammable and other dangerous substances. It is also responsible for conducting and sponsoring research, promoting training and providing an information and advisory service. It keeps under review the adequacy of the current legal requirements and submits to the Government proposals for new or revised regulations and approved codes of practice. The Commission has general oversight of the work of the Health and Safety Executive and has power to delegate to the Executive as its main operational arm.

The Executive is however a distinct statutory body with day-to-day responsibility for making arrangements for the enforcement of safety legislation and the Commission cannot give directions about the enforcement in any particular case other than by direction of the Secretary of State.

Health and safety legislation is enforced by the Executive and by local authorities (who principally inspect shops, warehouses and a variety of service industries). The Executive and local authorities perform their enforcement functions in accordance with any general directions or guidance respectively which the Commission may give them.

ADVISORY COMMITTEES The Commission makes substantial use of advisory committees, both 'subject' committees concerned with particular kinds of hazard, and Industry Advisory Committees looking across the board at the safety of their sectors (see below). These committees advise the Commission directly, particularly on the development of standards, and may, for example, propose new guidance or give advice on particular hazards or action to deal with them. Some report also to Secretaries of State, eg for Energy.

Industry Advisory Committees	**'Subject' Advisory Committees**
Agriculture Industry Advisory Committee	Advisory Committee on Dangerous Pathogens
Ceramics Industry Advisory Committee	
Construction Industry Advisory Committee	Advisory Committee on Dangerous Substances
Cotton and Allied Textiles Industry Advisory Committee	Advisory Committee on Genetic Modification
Education Service Advisory Committee	
Foundries Industry Advisory Committee	Advisory Committee on Releases to the Environment
Health Services Advisory Committee	
Oil Industry Advisory Committee	Occupational Health Advisory Committee
Paper and Board Industry Advisory Committee	Advisory Committee on the Safety of Nuclear Installations
Printing Industry Advisory Committee	Advisory Committee on Toxic Substances.
Railway Industry Advisory Committee	
Rubber Industry Advisory Committee.	

Annex 2 AGENCY AGREEMENTS

Under the Health and Safety at Work etc Act 1974 (HSWA), the Health and Safety Commission can make agreements with Government departments or others for them to perform functions on HSC/E's behalf and with any minister, department or other public authority for HSE to perform appropriate functions on their behalf. These agreements are known as 'agency agreements' and are listed below.

(i) **Arrangements under Section 11 of the Health and Safety at Work etc Act 1974**

Functions performed on behalf of the Health and Safety Commission by arrangement

The United Kingdom Atomic Energy Authority (UKAEA) and the Health and Safety Executive manage jointly a programme of research and development work relating to safety and reliability, carried out by the UKAEA Safety and Reliability Directorate, for the purpose of Section 1 of HSWA.

(ii) **Agreements under Section 13 of the Health and Safety at Work etc Act 1974**

Agents performing functions of the Health and Safety Commission or the Health and Safety Executive

(a) The National Radiological Protection Board performs such functions relating to ionising or other radiations as may be requested from time to time and provides information and advice concerning radiation hazards on request.

(b) The Gas and Oil Measurement Branch of the Department of Trade and Industry (formerly Department of Energy) performs HSE's enforcement functions with respect to the Gas Quality Regulations 1972.

Government departments for which the Commission or the Executive performs functions as an agent

(a) Department of Employment - administration and enforcement of the Employers' Liability (Compulsory Insurance) Act 1969.

(b) Department of Employment - granting of licences under the Ammonium Nitrate Mixtures Exemption Order 1967.

(c) Department of Employment - appointment of organisations to test, inspect and approve containers; and approval of examination schemes submitted by container owners, in accordance with provisions of the International Convention for Safe Containers, as implemented by the Freight Containers (Safety Convention) Regulations 1984.

(d) Department of Trade and Industry - provision of a testing and assessment service for flameproof apparatus constructed to the requirement of the United States Code of Federal Regulations, Chapter 1, Title 30, part 18. Electric motor driven mine equipment and accessories (formerly known as Schedule 2G).

(e) Department of Employment - provision of advice on gas safety and enforcement of the Gas Safety (Rights of Entry) Regulations 1983.

(f)   Department of the Environment and Scottish Office Environment Department - to give advice on the substances and quantities for which hazardous substances consent is required by regulations made under the Planning (Hazardous Substances) Act 1990. (Advice was last given in June 1987. The Commission plans to review this advice but decided in April 1991, with the agreement of the respective Secretaries of State, to defer this review until the outcome of the new 'Seveso' Directive on the control of major accidents hazards can also be considered.)

(g)   Minister of Agriculture, Fisheries and Food, Scottish Office, Welsh Office, Department of Employment, Department of the Environment and Department of Health - authorisation of persons to enforce Part III of the Food and Environment Protection Act 1985 in relation to contraventions of the Control of Pesticides Regulations 1986. Evaluation of applications for the approval of pesticides under the Food and Environment Protection Act 1985.

(h)   Department of the Environment, Scottish Office, Welsh Office - enforcement of the Control of Pollution (Supply and Use of Injurious Substances) Regulations 1986 to control the supply and use of polychlorinated biphenyls (PCBs) and polychlorinated triphenyls (PCTs).

(i)   Department of Transport - HSE's HM Railway Inspectorate monitors and investigates accidents and gives technical advice to the Secretary of State for Transport, who remains responsible to Parliament for railway passenger safety.

(j)   Department of Employment - following transfer of ministerial responsibility for offshore safety from the Secretary of State for Energy to the Secretary of State for Employment, HSE carried out safety functions relating to offshore installations and pipelines until they were fully transferred to HSC by primary legislation. This agreement remains in force following the Offshore Safety Act 1992 until Repeals and Modification Regulations made under that Act, which clarify the HSC/E duties, are in place.

(k)   Department of Trade and Industry (formerly Department of Energy) - HSE is responsible for the management and operation of the well consent regime and for giving consents on behalf of the Secretary of State (safety related aspects of the regime were transferred to HSC/E when they assumed responsibility for offshore safety).

(l)   Department of the Environment - enforcement of Part VI of the Environmental Protection Act 1990 in relation to the release and marketing of genetically modified organisms and environmental aspects of contained uses of 'larger' genetically modified organisms.

Annex 3   **LEGISLATIVE PROJECTS: WORK STARTED OR COMPLETED DURING THE YEAR**

WORK STARTED - REGULATIONS OR APPROVED CODES OF PRACTICE (ACoPs)

(a) International

Further regulations to implement various EC directives on **classification and labelling of dangerous substances and preparations** (including Approved Codes, Approved Lists and Approved Guide).

Regulations to implement the EC directives on **extractive industries (boreholes** and in **mines and quarries).**

Regulations to implement the EC directive on the **provision of safety signs** at work.

Regulations to implement the EC directive on the **placing on the market and supervision of transfers of explosives.**

Regulations to harmonise the current GB requirements for the **carriage of dangerous goods** with the relevant international agreements.

Regulations to implement EC directive on work at **temporary or mobile construction sites.**

(b) Domestic

Review of the body of **existing primary and secondary UK health and safety legislation** as part of the renewed Government-wide drive to **reduce burdens on business** especially **small businesses.**

Review of the legislation on **confined spaces.**

Review of the **Diving Operations at Work** Regulations 1981.

Review of the **Gas Quality** Regulations 1972 and 1983.

The **review and reform of UK offshore safety legislation** - four sets of regulations; **Emergency Response, Fire and Explosion Hazard Management, Design and Construction and Management and Administration.**

Regulations to **control the carriage of dangerous goods by rail** (including associated Approved Codes).

Regulations requiring the **production and validation of Railway Safety Cases** (including ACoPs).

Regulations on **Railways (Safety Critical Work).**

REGULATIONS SUBMITTED/ACoPS PUBLISHED

(a) International

Provision and Use of Work Equipment Regulations 1992.

The Genetically Modified Organisms (Contained Use) Regulations 1992.

COSHH Amendment Regulations 1992.

Control of Asbestos at Work (Amendment) Regulations 1992.

Asbestos (Prohibitions) Regulations 1992.

ACoP on **Control of Asbestos** at Work (2nd Edition).

ACoP on Work with **Asbestos Insulation, Asbestos Coating and Asbestos Insulating Board.**

COSHH General and Carcinogen ACoPs.

Health and Safety **(Display Screen Equipment)** Regulations 1992.

Public Information for Radiation Emergencies Regulations 1992.

Manual Handling Operations Regulations 1992.

Management of Health and Safety at Work Regulations 1992

Health and Safety (Miscellaneous Provisions) **(Metrication etc)** Regulations 1992.

Workplace (Health, Safety and Welfare) Regulations 1992 and ACoP.

Personal Protective Equipment at Work Regulations 1992.

The **Road Traffic (Carriage of Dangerous Goods and Substances)** (Amendment) Regulations 1992.

The **Road Traffic (Training of Drivers of Vehicles Carrying Dangerous Goods)** (Amendment) Regulations 1993.

(b) Domestic

The Notification of **Cooling Towers and Evaporative Condensers** Regulations 1992

The **Mines (Shafts and Winding)** Regulations 1993

The **Coal** and Other **Safety-Lamp Mines** Regulations 1992

Offshore Installations (Safety Case) Regulations 1992

CONSULTATIVE DOCUMENTS ISSUED - REGULATIONS OR ACOPS

(a) International

ACoP for the **Control of Biological Agents**: proposals for amendments to the **Control of Substances Hazardous to Health** Regulations 1988.

Proposed **Chemicals (Hazard Information and Packaging) (CHIP)** Regulations includes Approved Codes, Approved Lists and Approved Guide.

Proposals to amend **Control of Substances Hazardous to Health** Regulations and ACoPs.

Notification of New Substances Regulations.

Asbestos Worker Protection and Further Prohibitions Regulations and ACoPs.

Construction (Design and Management) Regulations and Approved Code of Practice.

(b) Domestic

ACoP on the **Prevention of Inrushes.**

Coal Mines (Owners Operating Rules) Regulations.

Mines (Shafts and Winding) Regulations.

Management and Administration of Safety and Health at Mines Regulations.

Offshore Safety (Repeals and Modifications) Regulations.

EUROPEAN COMMISSION LEGISLATIVE ACTIVITY

Figure 1 Proposals published by the EC during the period 1 April 1992 - 31 March 1993

Directive/Instrument	Date published in the Official Journal	Lead Department
Supervision and placing on the market of **explosives for civil uses and the mutual recognition of authorisations and approvals** relating to such explosives.	May 1992	HSE
Classification of biological agents (adds list to existing directive 90/679/EEC	July 1992	HSE
Appointment of officers for the prevention of the risks inherent in the carriage of dangerous goods in undertakings which transport such goods, and on the **vocational qualifications of such officers** (Articles 75 and 84).	September 1992	DoT
Protection of individuals with regard to the processing of personal data and on the free movement of such data. (Amendment to Articles 100A and 113).	November 1992	Home Office
Regulation on **shipments of radioactive substances within the Community.**	December 1992	HSE
Minimum safety and health requirements for transport activities and workplaces on means of transport (individual directive within the meaning of Article 16 of Directive 89/391/EEC).	January 1993	HSE
Approximation of the laws of Member States relating to **personal protective equipment (PPE)** (Amendment to 89/686/EEC)(Article 100A).	February 1993	DTI
Minimum safety and health requirements regarding exposure of workers to risks from **physical agents**.	December 1992	HSE

4

Figure 2 Directives progressed, or where common position or adoption was reached during the period 1 April 1992 - 31 March 1993

EC Number	Directive	Date of common position	Date adopted	Lead dept.
92/32/EEC	7th amendment to Directive 67/548/EEC on the approximation of laws, regulations and administrative provisions relating to the **classification, packaging and labelling of dangerous substances**		April 1992	HSE
92/37/EEC	16th adaption to technical progress of 67/548/EEC on **dangerous substances**		April 1992	HSE
92/58/EEC	Minimum requirements for the **provision of safety and/or health signs at work**		June 1992	HSE
92/57/EEC	Minimum safety and health requirements at **temporary or mobile construction sites**		June 1992	HSE
92/69/EEC	17th adaption to technical progress of 67/548/EEC on **dangerous substances**		July 1992	HSE
92/85/EEC	Health and safety at work of **pregnant workers** and **workers who have recently given birth or are breastfeeding**		October 1992	ED
92/91/EEC	Improving the safety and health protection of workers in the **extractive industries (boreholes)**		November 1992	HSE
92/104/EEC	Improving the safety and health protection of workers in **the extractive industries (mines and quarries)**		December 1992	HSE
93/15/EEC	Supervision and placing on the market of **explosives for civil uses and the mutual recognition of authorisations** relating to such explosives	April 1995		HSE
93/44/EEC	Council directive amending for the 2nd time Directive 89/392/EEC on the approximation of the laws of the Member States relating to **machinery** (Article 100A)	December 1992		DTI
93/21/EEC	18th adaptation to technical progress of 67/548/EEC (**Dangerous Substances** Directive).		November 1992	HSE

4

110

EC Number	Directive	Date of common position	Date adopted	Lead dept
Not yet available	19th Adaptation to technical progress of 67/548/EEC (Dangerous Substances Directive).	December 1992		HSE
	3rd Adaptation to technical progress of 88/479/EEC **(Dangerous Preparations** Directive**)**	February 1993		HSE
93/67/EEC	Principles for the **assessment of risks to man and the environment** of substances notified in accordance with Council Directive 67/548/EEC.	July 1993		HSE/DoE

4

SELECTED OUTPUT AND PERFORMANCE MEASURES BY FUNCTION

Functional category	Staff resources (years)			Major outputs			
	1990/91	1991/92	1992/93		1990/91	1991/92	1992/93

1 POLICY FORMATION

Work of HSC/E Committees and Boards Includes direct staff support for senior committees and subject advisory committees	36.6	42.0	37.4				
International Policy Projects Includes all domestic projects with a clear international connection or motive	110.2	130.0	153.0	See progress with legislative projects at Annexes 3 and 4			
Domestic Policy Projects May be legislative (leading to regulations) or non-legislative (leading to stand-alone guidance)	65.7	82.6	106.1				
Other Policy Work All policy work not specifically allocated to a project. Includes preparation of policy papers; liaising with external bodies; answering PQs and other correspondence; evaluating and monitoring NIGs; the work of the Economics and Statistics Unit	115.9	130.5	142.3				

2 MAIN PROGRAMMES

Planned Inspection Main category of preventive work by HSE's inspectorates	355.7	393.7	396.9	**Field Operations Division**			
				Planned inspections	165198	168865	157426
				Inspections/staff-year	496	493	467
				Mines Inspectorate			
				Planned inspections	3064	2462	2190
				Inspections/staff-year	180	167	195
				Offshore Safety Division[1]			
				Planned inspections	-	359	405
				Railway Inspectorate[2]			
				Planned inspections	-	2306	1452
				Inspections/staff-year	-	271	179
				Technology and Health Sciences Division			
				Planned inspections	243	285	459

Functional category	Staff resources (years)			Major outputs			
	1990/91	1991/92	1992/93		1990/91	1991/92	1992/93

Licence Monitoring — 67.6, 64.8, 65.7

Includes work of the Nuclear Installations Inspectorate in monitoring nuclear site licences; monitoring asbestos licences by Factory Inspectorate; and various licensing regimes for explosive production, storage and imports

Field Operations Division
- Asbestos licence applications processed — 416, 406, 278
- Petroleum licence applications processed — 225, 256, 91

Nuclear Installations Inspectorate
- Nuclear site inspections — 841, 793, 883
- Annual site emergency exercises — 47, 44, 44

Assessment of Systems and Designs — 153.9, 210.0, 220.0

Includes the examination of safety cases submitted by operators under the Nuclear Installations Acts and Control of Industrial Major Accident Hazard Regulations (CIMAH), and part of the work of the Accident Prevention Advisory Unit (APAU)

Field Operations Division
- Major hazards safety reports assessed — 60, 72, 144
- Planning applications (advice given) — 4749, 4823, 4790

Nuclear Safety Division
- Long term safety reports published — 1, 1, 0
- Quality assurance audits — 10, 10, 13
- Consents/approvals — 146, 101, 155

Offshore Safety Division[1]
- Offshore installation safety cases assessed — -, 1, 7
- Safety audits completed — -, 3, 10
- Well consents processed — -, 1300, 1274

Railway Inspectorate[2]
- Fixed works and rolling stock submissions considered — -, 237, 486

Strategy and General Division (Accident Prevention and Advisory Unit)
- Safety audits completed — 9, 8, 6

Technology and Health Sciences Division
- Major hazards safety cases assessed — 171, 119, 118
- Planning applications (advice given) — 678, 724, 699
- Fire certificates issued/updated — 32, 15, 20

Formal Enforcement and Court Activity — 65.9, 76.5, 77.8

All work connected with preparing and bringing prosecutions before the courts, and the issue and monitoring of prohibition and improvement notices

- Informations (prosecutions) — 2312, 2424, 2129 p
- Improvement and prohibition notices — 12758, 12419, 11857 p

Functional category	Staff resources (years)			Major outputs			
	1990/91	1991/92	1992/93		1990/91	1991/92	1992/93

3 PROGRAMMABLE ACTIVITIES

Functional category	1990/91	1991/92	1992/93	Major outputs	1990/91	1991/92	1992/93
Publications Work by Directorate of Information and Advisory Services (DIAS) connected with all HSE's publications	31.5	35.7	41.0	Publications produced	315	420	484
Planned Information Activity Work by DIAS to give publicity to HSE's messages about health and safety issues	9.0	10.7	12.5	Exhibitions/displays	60	100	259
				Lectures/demonstrations	168	100	192
				Press advertisements	140	200	336
Practical Study of Risks and Control Measures Includes most of HSE's research programme and other work to develop knowledge relevant to solving specific health and safety problems and making that knowledge available	191.8	234.5	248.8	**Nuclear Safety Division** Extramural projects placed	80	73	89
				Research and Laboratory Services Division Intramural research projects completed	21	19	44
				Papers approved for publication in scientific/technical press	57	56	88
				Internal reports produced	151	155	226
				Strategy and General Division (Research Strategy Unit) Extramural research projects completed	41	74	104
				Technology and Health Sciences Division Guidance documents published	13	14	48
				Epidemiological survey reports	2	2	3
Formation of British and International Standards Includes all work associated with the negotiations of international standards work to develop protocols and standards for certification work outside HSE	59.7	53.9	48.8	British and International Standards meetings attended	1464	1578	1604
Promotional Work Education of the informed public, safety professionals etc, about health and safety matters that may affect them	23.8	29.9	43.6				

5

4 SPECIAL INVESTIGATIONS/ INITIATIVES

	Staff resources (years)				Major outputs	1990/91	1991/92	1992/93
	35.8	47.9	69.9		**Field Operations Division**			

Work by the inspectorates and EMAS to ascertain the state of safety or health in a particular sector; to draw attention to new policy initiatives (eg as part of a major campaign); and to visit suppliers of equipment and substances to ensure compliance with requirements that they are safe for use at work

Field Operations Division

Major outputs	1990/91	1991/92	1992/93
Visits for special projects, campaigns and other initiatives	4549	5681	7720
Visits to manufacturers, importers and suppliers	3373	3185	3303
Mines Inspectorate			
Inspections for special projects	237	249	163

5 AGENCY AGREEMENTS

Staff resources: 0.9   0.5   0.0

Includes oversight of inspection arrangements for railways and offshore installations and work by NRPB in connection with ionising and non-ionising radiations

6 NATIONAL INTEREST GROUP ACTIVITY

Staff resources: 67.9   73.2   83.7

Work in providing centres of expertise for the standards affecting particular industries, including servicing HSC's Industry Advisory Committees

7 SERVICES TO INDUSTRY AND THE PUBLIC

Testing, Certification and Approval

Staff resources: 136.6   130.8   150.6

Work to satisfy statutory requirements that particular products or substances should be approved or certified by HSE before being marketed or used

Major outputs	1990/91	1991/92	1992/93
Field Operations Division			
Tractor cab and RPE approval/ exemption certificates issued	67	59	29
Mines Inspectorate			
Exemptions issued	1022	856	910
Research and Laboratory Services Division			
Jobs completed by the Electrical Equipment Certification Service	1206	1348	1399
Jobs/staff-year	26	25	27
Safety Policy Division			
Mining qualifications certificates issued	808	329	606

Functional category	1990/91	1991/92	1992/93	Major outputs	1990/91	1991/92	1992/93
				Technology and Health Sciences Division			
				Pesticides approved	354	470	365
				Notifications of new substances	510	521	571
				Tanker Approvals	191	329	46
Statutory Clinical Assessment and Medical Surveillance Includes examinations required by statute of workers exposed to specific hazards such as asbestos, and work by EMAS in approving and monitoring first aid training	37.3	31.8	14.1	**Field Operations Division (Employment Medical Advisory Service)** Referrals for medical advice Medical examinations of workers exposed to specific hazards	1508 1952	2681 2901	2040 2404
Occupational Health Advice Work by the Employment Medical Advisory Service to encourage the prevention of work-related disease and the promotion of better health in the workplace	31.0	38.3	50.8	**Field Operations Division (Employment Medical Advisory Service)** Advisory visits to outside organisations	2717	3174	3392
Civil Claims, Public Inquiries and Inquests	13.4	13.1	18.5				
Library and Public Information	40.0	43.2	45.2	Responses to enquiries from the public Free publications issued (million)	133000 7.0	175000 6.1	201291 8.2
Advisory Work To satisfy ad hoc enquiries and to give advice to industry on health and safety legislation	54.9	116.7	73.0	**Field Operations Division** Advisory visits Advisory contacts[3]	3140 -	4317 23445	- 41089

8 PUBLIC ACCOUNTABILITY

Functional category	1990/91	1991/92	1992/93	Major outputs	1990/91	1991/92	1992/93
Parliamentary and correspondence Secretariat work co-ordinating prompt and accurate replies to PQs and official correspondence	7.8	7.8	8.9	Parliamentary questions Formal correspondence cases	406 958	501 955	345 975
Press Office To ensure an informed reaction by the media to matters of public concern relevant to HSC/E's responsibilities and to stimulate awareness and understanding of health and safety issues	11.0	12.0	14.0	Press notices Press conferences/briefings held	234 35	286 32	338 47

Functional category	Staff resources (years)			Major outputs	1990/91	1991/92	1992/93
	1990/91	1991/92	1992/93				
9 INVESTIGATION OF ACCIDENTS AND COMPLAINTS	104.7	138.9	146.9	**Field Operations Division**			
				Accident/incident investigations	10318	9252	9382
				Complaint investigations	15539	13795	15090
				Total investigations/staff year	280	207	204
				Mines Inspectorate			
				Total investigations	1565	1278	1061
				Total investigations/staff year	156	147	166
				Offshore Safety Division[1]			
				Total investigations	-	89	170
10 MANAGEMENT OVERHEAD Senior staff and direct secretarial support time in managing the organisation and helping determine its policies	160.9	198.6	209.0				
11 PLANNING, FINANCE AND INFORMATION TECHNOLOGY Planning, monitoring and reporting on the use of the Executive's resources, and the maintenance, development and support of IT systems in HSE	217.3	237.5	257.9	IT Measures:			
				Terminals connected to the network	1447	1936	2462
				Mainframe computer users supported	885	1164	1224
				Office system users supported	1074	1247	1233
12 CENTRALISED COMMON SERVICES To provide relevant services that it is not cost-efficient to decentralise	241.5	271.6	304.0	Treasury typing units completed (thousand)	322	313	280
				Letters franked (thousand)	382	450	589
13 PERSONNEL SERVICES AND TRAINING	144.9	166.0	186.6	Career/management development interviews given by personnel staff	865	709	550
				Attendances at in-house training courses	4304	6406	8490
				Number of in-house courses run	386	676	929

5

14 TECHNICAL SUPPORT TO FIELD ACTIVITY Work by HSE's technical, scientific and medical staff in providing analytical and specialist support and advice to inspectors, and a forensic service independent of industry for any safety matter requiring investigation	249.6	193.3	232.1	Laboratory analyses Specialists' visits Visits in support of field work	157218 5358 2163	142629 6543 2465	113633 6539 2746
15 LEGAL SUPPORT To provide a service of legal support to the Commission and Executive	11.5	11.5	12.3				
16 ADMINISTRATIVE SUPPORT TO FIELD ACTIVITY Includes Inspectorates' HQ and field support staff	866.2	905.1	967.5	**Field Operations Division** Ratio field support staff to field professional staff	0.80	0.80	0.76
MISCELLANEOUS Work of the Railway Inspectorate which in 1990/91 was not classified into functional categories[1]	15.3	-	-				
Total	3736	4133	4439				

Notes
(1) HSE assumed responsibility for offshore safety on 1 April 1991.
(2) The Railway Inspectorate transferred from the Department of Transport on 3 December 1990.
(3) New output measure from 1 April 1991.

STATISTICS ON ENFORCEMENT ACTION AND PENALTIES

The following table gives a summary of HSE's enforcement activity since 1986/87. Fuller information, including the work of local authorities, can be found in the statistical supplement, tables 21 to 24. Annex 6 of the 1991/92 Annual Report set out HSE's approach to enforcement.

The bulk of HSE's prosecution work is undertaken by staff in the Field Operations Division and in 1992/93 they spent a total of 73.3 staff years on prosecution work, slightly more than planned. This was mainly because of a number of difficult and protracted prosecutions.

The average fine for all health and safety offences has risen by 17%, the largest rise for a number of years. This reflects the introduction in the lower courts on 6 March 1992 of an exemplary maximum fine of £20 000 for the more serious offences (breach of sections 2-6 of the Health and Safety at Work etc Act 1974 (HSWA) and failure to comply with a notice or court order) and from 1 October 1992 the increase from £2000 to £5000 of the maximum fine for other health and safety offences.

Both the number of informations laid and the number of notices issued have fallen. This is due in part to a change in emphasis in the subject matter of notices. Inspectors are now more frequently addressing organisational deficiencies which are the root causes of poor health and safety performance, rather than specific defects. An example would be the issuing of a notice requiring a maintenance system for machinery guards rather than individual notices for every dangerous machine. In addition, inspectors required training before the introduction of the 'six pack' of new health and safety regulations and following their introduction inspectors spent time discussing and explaining their implications with employers before resorting to formal enforcement measures.

The types of enforcement action referred to in the tables are defined as follows:

Improvement Notices require employers to take remedial action on specific breaches of the law within a specified time limit;

Prohibition Notices are issued in cases where the inspector believes that a work activity involves or will involve a risk of serious personal injury;

Immediate Prohibition Notices stop a work activity immediately until a risk is dealt with;

Deferred Prohibition Notices stop a work activity within a specified time, for example, because the risk of injury does not require action to control it, or where it would be unwise to interrupt a process in mid-cycle;

Informations laid (or 'charges preferred' in Scotland) are the first step in prosecution. They are a statement of the offence that is supposed to have been committed. Each information laid relates to a single offence. Particular cases which involve more than one offence therefore deal with multiple informations laid.

6

Figure 1 Enforcement action, prosecutions and notices issued by all enforcing authorities (excluding local authorities), 1986/87-1992/93(a)

Prosecutions	Total informations laid (b)	Informations where result recorded (b)	*of which* Convictions	Average penalty per conviction
1986/87	2199	2120	1771	£410
1987/88	2337	2337	2053	£792 (c)
1988/89	2328	2328	2090	£541
1989/90	2653	2653	2289	£783 (d)
1990/91	2312	2312	1991	£903 (e)
1991/92	2424	2424	2126	£1181 (f)
1992/93p	2129	2129	1843	£1384

Notices issued *by type*	Improvement	Deferred prohibition	Immediate prohibition	Total notices
1986/87	6577	196	2707	9480
1987/88	6631	234	4296	11161
1988/89	6693	189	4664	11546
1989/90	7610	200	4332	12142
1990/91	8489	227	4022	12738
1991/92	8395	222	3802	12419
1992/93p	7434	198	4225	11857

Notes
(a) Years commencing 1 April
(b) Includes, for Scotland, charges preferred.
(c) Includes fines totalling £750 000 imposed against BP. If these convictions are excluded the average fine for 1987/88 would be £427.
(d) Includes a fine of £100 000 imposed against Nobels Explosives. If this conviction was excluded the average fine for 1989/90 would be £739.
(e) Includes fines of £250 000 against Nobels Explosives and £100 000 against Tate and Lyle (reduced from £250 000 on appeal in November 1990). If these convictions were excluded the average fine for 1990/91 would be £728.
(f) Includes fines of £250 000 against British Rail and £100 000 against both Shell UK and British Gas. If these convictions were excluded, the average fine for 1991/92 would be £969.

Figures for average penalty are in current price terms not adjusted for inflation

p   provisional

120

Annex 7   EXPENDITURE AND STAFFING

Statement of expenditure

	1991/92	1992/93
Health and Safety Commission	*£000*	*£000*
Salaries etc	242	272
Travel, subsistence, conferences and general expenses	130	138
Total	372	410

Health and Safety Executive		
Salaries etc	84727	96884
Superannuation	13310	15276
Rent, rates, maintenance and other premises costs	17054	19341
Travel, removal, telephones and other general expenses	31731	37329
Vehicle maintenance, consumables and other miscellaneous expenses	2206	2558
Research, testing and agency services	26517	28632
Capital payments	18390	11361
Total	193935	211381
Total *Commission and Executive*	194307	211791

Notes
(1) The 1992/93 figures are provisional and have not been audited.
(2) The full income and expenditure accounts and balance sheet of the Commission and Executive will be
published as a White Paper early in 1994.

Total Health and Safety Executive staff by Division *For the Inspectorates, inspectors included in the total are shown in italics*[1]

	1.4.91 Staff in post		1.4.92 Staff in post		1.4.93 Staff in post	
Health and Safety Commission (support)	4		5		5	
Director General's Office	6		6		10	
Executive Support Branch[2]	28 [3]		-		-	
Accident Prevention Advisory Unit[2]	23		-		-	
Solicitor's Office	15.5		15.5		17	
Resources and Planning Division[4]						
Financial Control & Planning	108		67.5		72.5	
Directorate of Corporate Services	274.5		-		-	
Business Services Branch	-		295		322.5	
Human Resource Management Branch	-		137		143	
Computer and Systems Unit	60		-		-	
Directorate of Information and Advisory Services	105.5		127.5		127.5	
Hazardous Installations Policy Branch[5]	24.5		-		-	
Special Hazards Division[6]	71.5		-		-	
Safety Policy Division	-		117		124	
Safety and General Policy Division[6]	73		-		-	
Strategy and General Division	-		138		150.5	
Health Policy Division and Medical Services HQ [7,8,9,10]	176		112		89	
Field Operations Division[7]	1797		1904		1960.5	
HM Agricultural Inspectors	166		171		171.5	
HM Factory Inspectors	605		638.5		649	
HM Quarries Inspectors	12		13		13	
Doctors and nurses	93.5		100		108	
Specialist Inspectors	93		107.5		99	
Scientists	24.5		27.5		28.5	
Administrative support and other categories	803		846.5		891.5	
HM Railway Inspectorate[11]	34	*25*	52	*28*	63	*35*
HM Inspectorate of Mines	77	*43.5*	64	*37.5*	60	*30*
Offshore Safety Division[12]	88	*41*	226	*108*	319.5	*166.5*
HM Nuclear Installations Inspectorate	248	*161*	265.5	*167.5*	271.5	*169*
Technology Division[7,13]	215.5	*134.5*	-		-	
Technology and Health Sciences Division	-		320.5	*132.5*	333	*132*
Research and Laboratory Services Division[7]	397.5		415		415	
Electrical Equipment Certification Service	50.5		53.5		54	
Total	3877		4321		4537.5	

Notes
(1) Apart from where numbers are given for particular inspector categories, the figures in italics refer to all categories of inspector working within the specified Inspectorate/Division.
(2) Became part of the Strategy and General Division following an internal reorganisation in January 1992.
(3) Includes the Information Strategy Unit previously part of the Computer and Systems Unit.
(4) Resources and Planning Division was reorganised during 1991/92.
(5) Became part of the Safety Policy Division following an internal reorganisation in January 1992.
(6) Elements of the Division formed parts of the Safety Policy, Strategy and General, and Health Policy Divisions following an internal reorganisation in January 1992.
(7) On 2 April 1990 HSE's Field Force was reorganised to form the Field Operations Division. The new Division incorporated elements of a number of existing Divisions.
(8) With effect from November 1991 part of the Division was transferred to the Technology and Health Sciences Division.
(9) Elements of the Safety and General Policy and Special Hazards Divisions joined the Division following an internal reorganisation in January 1992.
(10) Medical Services Headquarters became part of Field Operations Division on 1 July 1992.
(11) HM Railway Inspectorate transferred from the Department of Transport on 3 December 1990.
(12) Responsibility for offshore safety was transferred from the Department of Energy on 1 April 1990.
(13) With effect from November 1991, an element of Health Policy Division was combined with Technology Division to form a new Technology and Health Sciences Division

Total Health and Safety Executive/Commission staff by occupational group[1]

Professional staff [2]	1.4.91 Staff in post	1.4.92 Staff in post	1.4.93 Staff in post
Nuclear Inspectors	162	169.5	175
Factory Inspectors	651	698.5	707.5
Agriculture Inspectors	177	183	182.5
Mines Inspectors	45.5	43.5	36.5
Quarries Inspectors	12	14	14
Specialist Inspectors	229.5	252	251
Railway Inspectors[3]	25	27	34
Offshore Inspectors[4]	40	82	131.5
Doctors and Nurses[5]	110	-	-
Doctors[5]	-	61.5	61.5
Nurses[5]	-	54	53
Scientists and Professional/Technological Officers	375	420	439
Other professional specialisms	75	94.5	103.5
Sub-total	1902	2099.5	2189

Other specialisms[6]			
Policy Managers	-	116	123.5
Admin Managers employed on operational programmes	-	84.5	100
Admin Managers employed on scientific programmes	-	16.5	19
Personnel, Training, Accommodation Managers	-	47	47.5
Planning and Financial Managers	-	22.5	24
Purchasing Managers	-	7	8
IT Managers	-	30	31
Publications, Publicity and Information Managers	-	5	6
Internal Audit and Management Services Managers	-	20.5	27.5

Executive Officers[6]	-	264	316.5

Support Staff[6]			
Clerical	-	971.5	1012.5
Secretariat and Typing	-	431.5	440
Industrial Grades	-	52.5	40
Other[7]	-	153	153
Sub-total[6]	1975	2221.5	2348.5

Total	3877	4321	4537.5

Notes
(1) Table includes inspectors on non-inspection duties (eg line management, contributing to policy or technical standards).
(2) Professional staff may work either in operational or in policy making functions. They are in general recruited directly by HSE.
(3) The Railway Inspectorate transferred from the Department of Transport on 3 December 1990.
(4) Responsibility for offshore safety was transferred from the Department of Energy on 1 April 1991.
(5) In previous years the figures for doctors and nurses have not been given separately.
(6) The analysis provided of these staff this year is on a revised basis which does not provide a direct comparison with previous years. Earlier years' figures are available in published Annual Reports.
(7) Includes office service staff and sandwich students.

AREA OFFICES

Area Address *Local authorities covered within each area*

1 South West Inter City House, Mitchell Lane, Victoria Street, Bristol BS1 6AN
Tel: 0272 290681 *Avon, Cornwall, Devon, Gloucestershire, Somerset, Isles of Scilly*

2 South Priestley House, Priestley Road, Basingstoke RG24 9NW. Tel: 0256 473181
Berkshire, Dorset, Hampshire, Isle of Wight, Wiltshire

3 South East 3 East Grinstead House, London Road, East Grinstead, West Sussex
RH19 1RR Tel: 0342 326922 *Kent, Surrey, East Sussex, West Sussex*

5 London North Maritime House, 1 Linton Road, Barking, Essex 1G11 8HF
Tel: 081 594 5522 *Barking, Barnet, Brent, Camden, Dagenham, Ealing, Enfield, Hackney, Harrow,
Havering, Islington, Newham, Redbridge, Tower Hamlets, Waltham Forest*

6 London South 1 Long Lane, London SE1 4PG. Tel: 071 407 8911
*Bexley, Bromley, City of London, Croydon, Greenwich, Hammersmith, Hillingdon, Hounslow, Kensington
and Chelsea, Kingston, Lambeth, Lewisham, Merton, Richmond, Southwark, Sutton, Wandsworth, City
of Westminster*

7 East Anglia 39 Baddow Road, Chelmsford, Essex CM2 0HL Tel: 0245 284661
Essex (except the London Boroughs in Essex covered by Area 5), Norfolk, Suffolk

8 Northern Home Counties 14 Cardiff Road, Luton, Bedfordshire LU1 1PP
Tel: 0582 34121 *Bedfordshire, Buckinghamshire, Cambridgeshire, Hertfordshire*

9 East Midlands Belgrave House, 1 Greyfriars Northampton NN1 2BS. Tel: 0604 21233
Leicestershire, Northamptonshire, Oxfordshire, Warwickshire

10 West Midlands McLaren Building, 2 Masshouse Circus, Queensway, Birmingham B4 7NP
Tel: 021 200 2299 *Birmingham, Coventry, Dudley, Sandwell, Solihull, Walsall, Wolverhampton*

11 Wales Brunel House, Fitzalen Road, Cardiff CF2 1SH. Tel: 0222 473777
Clwyd, Dyfed, Gwent, Gwynedd, Mid Glamorgan, Powys, South Glamorgan, West Glamorgan

12 Marches The Marches House, Midway, Newcastle-under-Lyme, Staffs ST5 1DT.
Tel: 0782 717181 *Hereford and Worcester, Shropshire, Staffordshire*

13 North Midlands Birbeck House, Trinity Square, Nottingham NG1 4AU. Tel: 0602 470712
Derbyshire, Lincolnshire, Nottinghamshire

14 South Yorkshire and Humberside Sovereign House, 40 Silver Street, Sheffield S1 2ES
Tel: 0742 739081 *Barnsley, Doncaster, Humberside, Rotherham, Sheffield*

15 West and North Yorkshire 8 St Paul's Street, Leeds LS1 2LE. Tel: 0532 446191
Bradford, Calderdale, Kirklees, North Yorkshire, Wakefield

16 Greater Manchester Quay House, Quay Street, Manchester M3 3JB. Tel: 061 831 7111
*Bolton, Bury, City of Manchester, City of Salford, Oldham, Rochdale, Stockport, Tameside, Trafford,
Wigan*

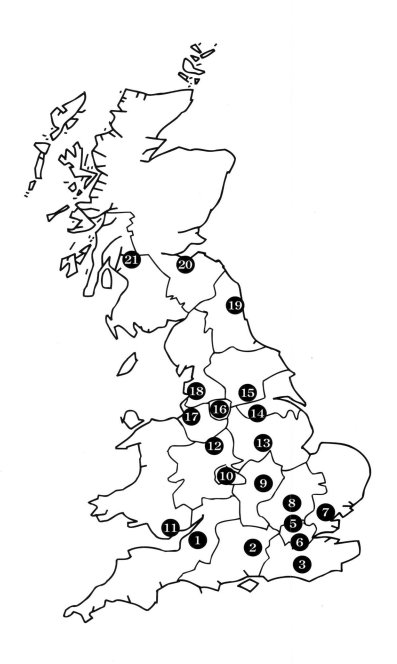

17 Merseyside   The Triad, Stanley Road, Bootle L20 3PG. Tel: 051 922 7211
Cheshire, Knowsley, Liverpool, St Helens, Sefton, Wirral

18 North West   Victoria House, Ormskirk Road, Preston PR1 1HH. Tel: 0772 59321
Cumbria, Lancashire.

19 North East   Arden House, Regent Centre, Gosforth, Newcastle-upon-Tyne NE3 3JN
Tel: 091 284 8448   *Cleveland, Durham, Gateshead, Newcastle-upon-Tyne, North Tyneside, Northumberland, South Tyneside, Sunderland*

20 Scotland East: Belford House, 59 Belford Road, Edinburgh EH4 3UE. Tel: 031 247 2000
Borders, Central Fife, Grampian, Highland, Lothian, Tayside and the Island areas of Orkney and Shetland.

21 Scotland West   314 St Vincent Street, Glasgow G3 8XG. Tel: 041 204 2646
Dumfries and Galloway, Strathclyde, the Western Isles.

NATIONAL INTEREST GROUPS

Area		Interest
01	South West	*Health Services*
02	South	*Crown, Fire and Police*
03	South East	*Paper and Board*
05	London North	*Education, Printing and Bookbinding*
06	London South	*Construction, Air Transport*
07	East Anglia	*Docks, Harbours, Water Treatment*
08	Northern Home Counties	*Woodworking, Concrete and Cement*
09	East Midlands	*Plastics, Leather and Footwear, Livestock and Stationary Machinery*
10	West Midlands	*Engineering*
11	Wales	*Molten Metals*
12	Marches	*Ceramics*
13	North Midlands	*Public Utilities, Agriculture- Crop Production*
14	South Yorkshire and Humberside	*Hazardous Installations and Transport*
15	West and North Yorkshire	*Wool, Textiles, Clothing, Laundries and Dry Cleaning, Mineral Fibres*
16	Greater Manchester	*Cotton, Rubber*
17	Merseyside	*Chemicals, Glass*
18	North West	*Local Government and Entertainment Services and Fairgrounds*
19	North East	*Shipbuilding, Ship-repairing, Heavy Fabrication and Welding*
20	Scotland East	*Drinks and Packaging, Forestry, Agriculture, Allied Industries*
21	Scotland West	*Food*

8

Annex 9 **SELECTED HSC/E PUBLICATIONS**

PRICED   *The health and safety system in Great Britain*   1992   ISBN 0 7176 0497 7
(formerly ISBN 0 11 886352 5)   £5.00

Local authorities report on health and safety in the service industries 1991/92 1993
ISBN 011 882121 0 £5.75

Appleton Inquiry Report (Report of an Inquiry into health and safety aspects of stoppages
caused by fire and bomb alerts on London Underground, British Rail and other mass transit
systems) 1993 ISBN 0 11 886394 0 £4.25

Electricity at work - safe working practices HS(G)85 1993 ISBN 0 7176 0442 X
(formerly ISBN 0 11 882081 8)   £3.50

The responsibilities of school governors for health and safety 1992 ISBN 0 7176 0436 5
(formerly ISBN 0 11 886337 1)   £3.50

Farm wise: your guide to health and safety 1992 ISBN 0 7176 0436 5
(formerly ISBN 0 11 882107 5) £3.50

Health and safety in retail and wholesale warehouses HS(G)76 1992 ISBN 0 7176 0445 4
(formerly ISBN 0 11 885731 2) £4.25

A guide to the Public Information for Radiation Emergencies Regulations 1992
ISBN 0 7176 0515 9 (formerly ISBN 011 8863509) £5.00

Sick building syndrome: a review of the evidence of causes and solutions HSE Contract Research
Report No 42/1992 1992 ISBN 0 7176 0591 4 (formerly ISBN 0 11 886364 9) £25.00

List of Authorised Explosives 1992 ISBN 0 7176 0646 5 (formerly ISBN 0 11 886396 7) £7.75

The Road Tanker Approved List 1992   ISBN 0 7176 0553 1 (formerly ISBN 0 11 886314 2)
£7.00

A framework for the restriction of occupational exposure to ionising radiation HS(G)91   1992
ISBN 0 7176 0499 3 (formerly ISBN 011 886324 X) £3.50

A Guide to the Genetically Modified Organisms (Contained Use) Regulations 1992 L29 1993
ISBN 0 7176 0473 X (formerly ISBN 0 11 882049 4) £5.00

The occupational zoonoses 1993 ISBN 0 7176 0517 5 (formerly ISBN 0 11 88639 7) £5.00

Veterinary medicines: safe use by farmers and other animal handlers HS(G)86   1992
ISBN 0 11 886361 4 £3.50

Training woodworking machinists HS(G)83 1992 ISBN 0 7176 0549 3
(formerly ISBN 0 11 886316 9) £4.00

Fire safety in the printing industry 1992 ISBN 0 7176 0559 0
(formerly ISBN 0 11 886375 4) £6.00

9

Health and safety in animal facilities 1992 ISBN 0 11 886353 3 £4.00

The problems of asbestos removal at high temperatures EH57   1993 ISBN 0 11 885586 7 £3.00

Shopping trolleys: safe system of work guidance HS(G)84 1992 ISBN 0 11 886326 6 £4.00

FREE   *Your patients and their work: an introduction to occupational health for family doctors*

A guide to producing a farm COSHH assessment IAC/L81

Passive smoking at work IND(G)63L (revised)

Drug abuse at work IND(G)91L (revised)

Electric storage batteries: safe charging and use IND(G)139L

The do's and don'ts of dry cleaning IND(G)131L

HSC/E publications are available from:
HSE Books (see back cover)

9

Annex 10 GLOSSARY OF ABBREVIATIONS

ACDP	Advisory Committee on Dangerous Pathogens
ACDS	Advisory Committee on Dangerous Substances
ACoP	Approved Code of Practice
ACGM	Advisory Committee on Genetic Modification
ACRE	Advisory Committee on Releases to the Environment
ACSNI	Advisory Committee on the Safety of Nuclear Installations
ACTS	Advisory Committee on Toxic Substances
AEA	Atomic Energy Authority
AIAC	Agriculture Industry Advisory Committee
APAU	Accident Prevention Advisory Unit
BCC	British Coal Corporation
BNFL	British Nuclear Fuels Limited
BS	British Standard
BSE	Bovine Spongiform Encephalopathy
BSI	British Standards Institution
CAPS	Computer Aiding the Planning System
CBI	Confederation of British Industry
CDM	Construction Design and Management Regulations
CEC	Commission of the European Communities
CEN	Comité Européen de Normalisation
CERIAC	Ceramics Industry Advisory Committee
CHEMAG	Chemicals in Agriculture Working Group
CHIP	Chemicals Hazard Information and Packaging Regulations
CIMAH	Control of Industrial Major Accident Hazards Regulations
CNC	Computer Numerical Control
CONIAC	Construction Industry Advisory Committee
COPR	Control of Pesticides Regulations
CORGI	Council for Registered Gas Installers
COSHH	Control of Substances Hazardous to Health Regulations
DoE	Department of the Environment
DoT	Department of Transport
DPS	Directorate of Purchasing and Supply
DTI	Department of Trade and Industry
EC	European Community
EECS	Electrical Equipment Certification Service
ELCTEX	Enforcement Liaison Certification for Transport of Explosives
EMAS	Employment Medical Advisory Service
ESAC	Education Services Advisory Committee
EYSHH	European Year of Safety Hygiene and Health at Work
FM	Finance Managers
FOCUS	Field Operations Computer System
FOD	Field Operations Division
GMO	Genetically Modified Organism

10

HELA	HSE/Local Authority Enforcement Liaison Committee
HF	Hydrogen Fluoride
HMIP	Her Majesty's Inspectorate of Pollution
HRD	Human Resource Development
HSC	Health and Safety Commission
HSE	Health and Safety Executive
HSAC	Health Service Advisory Committee
HSWA	Health and Safety at Work Act
IAEA	International Atomic Energy Agency
ILO	International Labour Organisation
IRR	Ionising Radiations Regulations
IT	Information Technology
JSC	Joint Standing Committee
LEA	Local Enterprise Agency
LEC's	Local Enterprise Companies
LTSR's	Long Term Safety Reviews
MCI	Management Charter Initiative
MEL	Maximum Exposure Limits
MoD	Ministry of Defence
NAO	National Audit Office
NCVQ	National Council for Vocational Qualifications
NIG	National Industry Group
NII	Nuclear Installations Inspectorate
NRT	National Responsibility Team
NSD	Nuclear Safety Division
OECD	Organisation of Economic Co-operation and Development
OES	Occupational Exposure Standard
OHSLB	Occupational Health and Safety Lead Bodies
OPM's	Output and Performance Measures
OSD	Offshore Safety Division
PIAC	Printing Industry Advisory Committee
PTOs	Power Take-off Shafts
PTW	Permit to Work
PWR	Pressurised Water Reactor
RAMG	Regulatory Assistance Management Group
RIAC	Railway Industry Advisory Committee
RIDDOR	Reporting of Injuries Diseases and Dangerous Occurrences Regulations
RUBIAC	Rubber Industry Advisory Committee
SAP's	Safety Assessment Principles
SBS	Sick Building Syndrome
SWA	Scotch Whisky Association

10

TEC	Training Enterprise Council
TFPI	Tripartite Forum on Health and Safety in the Pharmaceutical Industry
TOR	Tolerability of Risk
TQ	Total Quality
UKAEA	United Kingdom Atomic Energy Authority
UN	United Nations
VDU	Visual Display Unit
VSC	Voluntary Safety Cases
VWF	Vibration White Finger
WATCH	Working Group for the Assessment of Toxic Chemicals
WHO	World Health Organisation

10

Printed in the UK for the Health and Safety Executive
11/93   C50